THE 11ᵀᴴ COMMANDMENT

EXPERIENCING THE ONE ANOTHERS OF SCRIPTURE

don j. mcminn, ph.d.

© 6Acts Press
2322 creekside circle south
irving, tx 75063
972.432.8690
6Acts@6Acts.org
www.6Acts.org

The 11th Commandment

Experiencing the One Anothers of Scripture

Don J. McMinn

First edition—2000
2322 Creekside Circle South, Irving, Texas, 75063
972.432.8690

Printed in the United States for Worldwide Distribution
ISBN: 0-9703229-0-9
Library of Congress Catalog Number: 00-192599

TABLE OF CONTENTS

PAGE

CHAPTER 1 *9/7 JML* THE 11ᵀʰ COMMANDMENT 1

CHAPTER 2 *9/14 JML* PREFER ONE ANOTHER 19

CHAPTER 3 *9/24 JML* ACCEPT ONE ANOTHER 31

CHAPTER 4 *9/31 RR* GREET ONE ANOTHER 45

CHAPTER 5 *10/7 RR* ENCOURAGE ONE ANOTHER 61

CHAPTER 6 *10/14 RR* COMFORT ONE ANOTHER 75

CHAPTER 7 *10/21 RR* CARRY ONE ANOTHER'S BURDENS 89

CHAPTER 8 *10/28 JML* FORGIVE ONE ANOTHER 99

CHAPTER 9 *11/4 ROBERT* ADMONISH ONE ANOTHER 111

CHAPTER 10 *JON WMS 11/11* EIGHT MORE ONE ANOTHERS 127

11/18 JML Wait for–Offer Hospitality to–Pray for–Rejoice with–Be Kind to–Honor–Confess Your Sins to–Be Devoted to   *11/25 JML*

ENDWORD

11ᵀʰ COMMANDMENT PROJECT

NOTES

DEDICATION

This first edition of the 11th Commandment workbook is lovingly dedicated to my friend Gene Lucas – a man of faith, vision and initiative.

Gene, thank you for our friendship.

—Don

THE 11ᵀᴴ COMMANDMENT

Experiencing the One Anothers of Scripture

This workbook begins in an unusual way—asking you, the reader, two questions. It's important that you take the time to think about your answers and then to write down your responses.

Question #1—Consider all the people you have known throughout your life. Which one person do you feel has genuinely loved you the most?

Person's name _____

Question #2—What did this person *do* to make you feel loved? [Use active verbs.]

This person _____ me.
This person _____ me.
This person _____ me.
This person _____ me.

We'll return to these answers later. Now, continue reading the remainder of this chapter.

The 11ᵗʰ Commandment

Since the days of Moses, the Jewish faith and religion centered on the Decalogue—the Ten Commandments God gave to Moses on Mt. Sinai. These ten laws were indelibly etched on the hearts and minds of every orthodox Jew, and they became the basis of their moral and religious belief system.

Imagine then the stir that Jesus must have caused when, during his final conversation with the disciples, he announced a new commandment, essentially the 11ᵗʰ Commandment. This new commandment, recorded in John 13:34-35, challenged the disciples with a new paradigm. His statement was significant and strategic.

One phrase at a time, his new command says:

- "Love one another."
- "As I have loved you, so you must love one another."
- "All men will know that you are my disciples if you love one another."

Jesus issued a:

- **declaration**—love one another
- **design**—as I have loved you
- **distinction**—your love for others will be the distinguishing mark of God on your lives.

GIVE BACK GROUND

I'm sure the disciples must have sensed the gravity of Jesus' statement, but at the same time, I think they might have been a bit frustrated. Love is, after all, a big concept that defies simple definition. Trying to describe love is like attempting to define the universe. And if the definition of love is challenging, the actual *doing* of love is even more so. Telling someone to "go love" is like telling him to "go wrap your arms around an elephant." It's just too big a task. We're likely to do nothing because the assignment seems elusive and unclear.

To experience the frustration of trying to define love, write your own definition:

Love is: _____.

That's why I suspect that the disciples, upon hearing the new command, might have wondered, "Master, your new commandment is beautifully said, but, uh, *how* do we love one another?"

Jesus' new command was, and is, extremely important. Regardless of the ambiguity that may surround the concept, we must grapple with the term because of the critical role that love plays in the kingdom of God. Love is, after all, the greatest of all grace gifts.

WHY LOVE IS SO IMPORTANT

LOVE SHOWS WORLD WE ARE HIS DISCIPLES (JN 13:35)

- Love is greater than faith and hope (1 Corinthians 13:13).
- All other commandments are summed up in the one command: "Love your neighbor as yourself" (Romans 13:9).
- Without love, acts of ministry are meaningless (1 Corinthians 13:1–3).
- Love is the fulfillment of the law (Romans 13:10).
- Love is the attribute by which God is described: "God is love" (1 John 4:16).

Ignore love, and you'll have no part in the kingdom of God.

But how can love be practically explained and demonstrated? When God says, "Love one another," what are we to *do*? Is love more than an ethereal concept or a heightened feeling?

My theory is this: The mysterious "how-to" of love is practically explained by the One Anothers of Scripture. We demonstrate love by engaging in the One Anothers.

The One Anothers of Scripture

Thirty-five times in the New Testament, we see a recurring word pattern—an action verb followed by the words "one another." Notice that the 11th Commandment includes this word pattern: "Love one another." I believe that this particular One Another (the 11th Commandment) is the overarching term under which the others fall. In biological terms, Love One Another is the genus, and the remaining thirty-four One Anothers are the species. In other words, in John 13:34, any one of the One Anothers could be substituted for the word *love*.

Later in this chapter we'll list all thirty-five of the One Anothers, but for now let's begin with three of them and see if they fit the template of John 13:34-35:

- "Comfort one another" (2 Corinthians 1:4).
- "Forgive one another" (Colossians 3:13).
- "Accept one another" (Romans 15:7).

Substituting these three verbs for the word *love*, we get:

- *Comfort, forgive,* and *accept* one another.
- As I have *comforted, forgiven,* and *accepted* you, so you must *comfort, forgive,* and *accept* one another.
- All men will know that you are my disciples if you *comfort, forgive,* and *accept* one another.

Am I taking liberties with the Scriptures? Not if the substitutions can be validated with other Scripture references.

Comfort One Another

In 2 Corinthians 1:3–4, we read that God is the God of all comfort who comforts us so we can comfort others. There's the:

- **declaration**—comfort others, and the
- **design**—as God has comforted us.

In John 11, we see that comforting others is a **distinguishing** characteristic of the life of Christ. Jesus went to the tomb of his friend Lazarus and when he saw Mary and her friends weeping, he was "deeply moved in spirit and troubled" (v. 33). Then comes the shortest verse in the Bible: "Jesus wept" (v. 35). Jesus identified so thoroughly with Mary and Martha's sorrow that he began to weep with them. This is the essence of comfort: empathizing so deeply with someone that you enter into her pain. Jesus was *not* weeping because Lazarus was dead; he had already declared that he would raise him up. Jesus was weeping because his friends were hurting. With his tears he comforted them. When the crowd at the tomb saw Jesus crying, they said, "See how he loved him!" (v. 36). The Jews were convinced of Jesus' love for Mary and Martha because he was willing to comfort them.

Forgive One Another

Colossians 3:13 says, "Forgive as the Lord forgave you." There's the:

- **declaration**—forgive others, and the
- **design**—as God has forgiven you.

In Mark 15, we see how forgiveness is a **distinguishing** characteristic of the life of Christ. While Jesus was on the cross, he said, "Father, forgive them." A centurion, standing post at the foot of the cross, heard Jesus' dying statements and was deeply touched by what he heard: "When the centurion, who stood there in front of Jesus, heard his cry and saw how he died, he said, 'Surely this man was the son of God!'" (v. 39) The centurion was convinced of the deity of Christ when he observed him forgiving others.

Accept One Another

In Romans 15:7, we read, "Accept one another, then, just as Christ accepted you." There's the:

- **declaration**—accept one another, and the
- **design**—as God has accepted you.

In John 4, we see accepting others as a **distinguishing** characteristic of Jesus' life. While resting at Jacob's well, Jesus initiated a conversation with a Samaritan woman. In first-century Jewish culture that was a radical initiative. Men typically didn't bother to talk to women because women were thought to be inferior to men. Jews certainly didn't interact with Samaritans, and this particular woman was a noted "sinner" (she had been married five times and was currently living with a man who was not her husband). But Jesus ignored all the prejudicial customs of his day and accepted her. His acceptance had a profound effect on her life and no doubt played a significant part in her coming to believe that he was the Son of God.

The One Anothers

I believe that the remaining thirty-one One Anothers would also fit the template. Each one includes the declaration, the design, and the distinguishing mark that love will make on our lives. Indeed, the One Anothers begin to define what love "looks like," and they provide a very practical methodology for how we can love others. They are the "how-to" of fulfilling the 11th Commandment.

Turn back to page 1, on which you recorded the name of the person who you feel has loved you the most and what that person *did* that made you feel loved. I think you will find that most, if not all, of the verbs that you wrote down are among the thirty-five verbs listed in the One Anothers.

Here is a list of the One Anothers. Compare the two lists and circle the One Anothers that were on your personal list.

1. Love one another (John 13:34).
2. Depend on one another (Romans 12:5 AMP).
3. Be devoted to one another (Romans 12:10).
4. Wash one another's feet (John 13:14).
5. Rejoice with one another (Romans 12:15; 1 Corinthians 12:26).
6. Weep with one another (Romans 12:15).
7. Live in harmony with one another (Romans 12:16).
8. Don't judge one another (Romans 14:13).
9. Accept one another (Romans 15:7).
10. Admonish one another (Colossians 3:16).
11. Greet one another (Romans 16:16).
12. Wait for one another (1 Corinthians 11:33).
13. Care for one another (1 Corinthians 12:25).
14. Serve one another (Galatians 5:13).
15. Be kind to one another (Ephesians 4:32).
16. Forgive one another (Ephesians 4:32; Colossians 3:13).
17. Be compassionate toward one another (Ephesians 4:32).
18. Encourage one another (1 Thessalonians 5:11).
19. Submit to one another (Ephesians 5:21).
20. Bear with one another (Ephesians 4:2; Colossians 3:13).
21. Stimulate love in one another (Hebrews 10:24).
22. Offer hospitality to one another (1 Peter 4:9).
23. Minister gifts to one another (1 Peter 4:10).
24. Be clothed in humility toward one another (1 Peter 5:5).
25. Don't slander one another (James 4:11).
26. Don't grumble against one another (James 5:9).
27. Confess your sins to one another (James 5:16).
28. Pray for one another (James 5:16).
29. Fellowship with one another (1 John 1:7).
30. Don't be puffed up against one another (1 Corinthians 4:6).
31. Carry one another's burdens (Galatians 6:2).
32. Honor one another (Romans 12:10).
33. Instruct one another (Romans 15:14).
34. Prefer one another (Romans 12:10).
35. Comfort one another (2 Corinthians 1:4).

In banking terms,

God deposited all he had in Jesus
and then opened up branch offices in every believer.

Foundational Principles of the One Anothers

To better understand how the One Anothers "work," let's discuss a few basic principles.

1. God is the source of the One Anothers.

"Love comes from God" (1 John 4:7).

God is the source of the One Anothers. John says, "We love because he first loved us" (1 John 4:19). If and when we are able to love others, it is only because we have first received love from God.

James teaches the same truth when he says, "*Every good and perfect gift is from above*, coming down from the Father of the heavenly lights, who does not change like shifting shadows" (James 1:17; emphasis added).

David, king of Israel, expressed this truth when he said, "But who am I, and who are my people, that we should be able to give as generously as this? *Everything comes from you*, and we have given you only what comes from your hand" (1 Chronicles 29:14; emphasis added).

God is the source of the One Anothers by virtue of the fact that he *is* love (1 John 4:16). His character exudes the One Anothers.

Though the One Anothers are actions that we do, they eventually become aspects of who we are. For example, I am to accept others, but the end goal is for me to become an *accepting* person. I am to comfort others, but eventually, I want to become an *empathizing* person. As I continually greet others, I will become a *friendly, approachable* person.

You might ask, "Shouldn't we *become* first and then *do*? Shouldn't our acts be motivated by who we are?" That may be the ideal, but developmentally, the best way to become something is first to practice the desired action. If we *do* what we know is right, we will eventually *become* what we need to become. Eventually, our actions will be motivated by who we are.

But God is not confined to this conditioning process. First John 4:16 states that God *is* love, therefore his loving acts are simply an overflow of who he is. He comforts us because he is, in his character, empathetic. He accepts us because he is the essence of acceptance.

"Love comes from God."

2. God has two channels of distribution—himself and others.

"Since God so loved us, we also ought to love one another" (1 John 4:11).

God is the source of all things good and perfect (James 1:17), but where does he "store" these commodities, and how does he distribute them?

First, God placed his fullness of love in Jesus Christ (Colossians 1:19). Then God placed Jesus in every member of his body: "Christ in you, the hope of glory" (Colossians 1:27).

In banking terms, God deposited all he had in Jesus and then opened up branch offices in every believer.

God has a dual-distribution system:

"Since God so loved us, we also ought to love one another."

God often meets our needs directly. First Samuel 20–30 chronicles a difficult time in David's life. He was on the run from Saul, who had a warrant out for his arrest—dead or alive. His traveling companions were ruthless, rough men, and he was separated from his friends and family. David's troubles went from bad to worse when, while he was trying to help Achish, the Amalekites raided his camp and kidnapped his family and the families of his men. His comrades spoke of insurrection. David was hurting and in deep trouble.

What did he do? "David found strength in the Lord his God" (1 Samuel 30:6). David went directly to God and received what he needed.

At times, the apostle Paul also went directly to the Lord: "No one came to my support, but everyone deserted me. But the Lord stood at my side and gave me strength" (2 Timothy 4:16–17).

When we have a pressing need, we can go directly to God and receive what we need directly from him.

Write about a time when God met your needs directly:

_____

_____

_____

God often meets our needs through other people.
Though God can meet our needs directly, he often chooses to use other people. We just saw how David received support and comfort directly from God, but at other times, when David had a need, God chose to distribute his provision through another human.

- When David needed to be admonished, God used Nathan (2 Samuel 12).
- When David needed encouragement, God used Jonathan (1 Samuel 20).
- When David needed support, God used Ahimelech, the priest (1 Samuel 21).
- When David needed comfort, God used his friends (2 Samuel 15:30).

God often meets our needs through other people.

In like manner, God often met the apostle Paul's needs through other people. For instance, God often called upon the church at Philippi to minister to Paul. The apostle spoke of this support: "It was good of you to share in my troubles" (Philippians 4:14).

Often, the One Anothers will flow from God through multiple channels. Second Corinthians 7:6–7 tells of four generations of comfort: God comforted the Corinthian church, who in turn comforted Titus, who then comforted Paul. The same transfer is seen regarding encouragement in 2 Corinthians 7:13: Paul was encouraged because the Corinthians had encouraged Titus.

Often, our heartfelt needs are best met when God ministers to us through another human being. Most of us understand, intellectually, that God accepts, encourages, and comforts us, but sometimes, we don't sense, emotionally, that these needs are being met until someone with flesh and blood ministers to us.

The need for a flesh-and-blood person to help us is illustrated in a familiar story. One night, a frightened young boy called out in the stillness of the night, "Daddy, I'm scared!" His father responded, "Honey, don't be afraid, Daddy's right across the hall." After a brief pause, the little boy said, "I'm still scared," to which the father added, "You don't need to be afraid. God is with you. God loves you." After a longer pause, the boy said, "Daddy, I'm still scared. I want someone with skin on!"

Indeed, sometimes we need someone "with skin on" to meet our needs. This truth was epitomized in the incarnation of Jesus. "The Word became flesh and made his dwelling among us" (John 1:14). It was difficult for Old Testament saints to visualize or to experience the fullness of God's love because he was in heaven and seemed far removed. But in Jesus, God's ambassador to the human race, the world witnessed and experienced the loving heart of God. God still demonstrates his love through appointed ambassadors—except now the ambassador is not Jesus, it is you and me.

> The term "one another" is a reciprocal pronoun, implying that there are two or more parties who are acting equally to one another.

Write about a time when God met your needs through another person:

_____

_____

_____

3. **God has a unique "economic plan" for distributing the One Anothers.**

An old Jewish tale tells of a rabbi who asked God to show him heaven and hell. The Lord, opening the door to a room, said to him, "First I will show you hell." Inside, the rabbi saw a group of people sitting around a large, round table, grumbling and complaining. On the table was a bowl of delicious stew. Each person had a spoon, but the handle was longer than a person's arm. So the people could dip the stew from the bowl but could not bring it to their mouths. Their bodies were emaciated, and they were frustrated and angry.

"Now," the Lord said, taking the rabbi to another room, "I will show you heaven." He opened the door to a room identical to the first. But here, the people were well nourished, joyful, and talking among themselves. They, too, had long-handled spoons but had apparently overcome the problem. The rabbi was perplexed by what he saw.

The Lord explained, "These have learned to feed each other."

According to this tale, the people in heaven flourished in an atmosphere of giving and receiving. They had fully grasped the meaning of Jesus' words, "It is more blessed to give than to receive" (Acts 20:35) and were basking in the wonder of his command, "Give, and it will be given to you" (Luke 6:38).

This story speaks eloquently of a fundamental truth: Divine commodities (the One Anothers) cannot be selfishly taken; they must be graciously given and received. God made us such that we cannot feed ourselves and be satisfied; we cannot meet our own needs and be fulfilled. There's plenty of food at the table, but we must "look not only to [our] own interests, but also to the interests of others" (Philippians 2:4).

The story also speaks of the reciprocal aspect of the One Anothers. The term "one another" is a reciprocal pronoun (as is the phrase "each other"), implying that there are two or more parties who are acting equally to one another. A reciprocal situation is one in which one person does for another what the other person does for him. For the "One Anothers" to work as they should, there must be reciprocity. We must give, and we must receive.

What hinders us from wanting to give to others?

_____

What hinders us from being willing to receive from others?

_____

Either and both of these vices will short-circuit God's economic plan of giving and receiving. Write about your struggle with both areas:

_____

_____

Divine Principles of God's Economic Plan

1. **Receiving must precede giving because we can't give what we don't have.**

"For I received from the Lord what I also passed on to you" (1 Corinthians 11:23).

This is an obvious truth, but it is one that is often overlooked. We simply cannot give what we have not received.

I once made a hospital visit with one of my young interns. Before we entered the patient's room, I told him that the person we were visiting was in intense pain and, at an appropriate moment, I wanted him to comfort her. He looked at me with a combination of confusion and anxiety. I immediately realized that he didn't know how to comfort someone; he didn't know what to say or do. Not wanting to embarrass him or to neglect the patient, I told him that I would do the comforting; he just needed to observe. We entered the room, and I ministered comfort.

My young friend didn't know how to comfort others because he had never been comforted. He couldn't give comfort because he had never received it. I then decided that part of my ministry to him would be to share in his pain and to comfort him. Then he would be equipped to minister in like manner to others.

Receiving requires humility. We must admit that we need comfort, acceptance, forgiveness, etc. before we will be willing to receive. Most of us struggle with self-reliance and self-sufficiency, both of which eclipse our desire and ability to receive.

Receiving produces gratefulness. Once we admit our need and freely receive from God and others, we will be overcome by gratefulness. In 430 B.C., the historian Thucydides wrote, "It was in those who had recovered from the plague that the sick and the dying found most compassion."[1] When we need one of the One Anothers and someone lovingly meets our need, we are then motivated by gratitude to give to others.

Because we must first receive before we can give, we are simply stewards of "God's grace in its various forms" (1 Peter 4:10). We simply give to others what he has given to us. Understanding this principle of stewardship should eliminate our pride—we're simply distributing God's resources, not our own.

If we seek him, the Holy Spirit will reveal to us how much God has given. "We have received the Spirit who is from God, that we may understand what God has freely given us" (1 Corinthians 2:12). We are often ignorant of all that God has given us; his abundant provision may be present, but we remain unaware. The Holy Spirit will tell us. As we yield to him and spend time in meditation and prayer, the Spirit will surprise us by revealing the abundance of what we have been given.

At the beginning of this chapter, I asked you to write down the name of a person who has genuinely loved you. My response would be—my mother. Mom consistently and unconditionally loved me. In large part, I am able to love others because of the love I received from her. So throughout this workbook, whenever we study a particular One Another, I'm going to share a personal anecdote about how my mother loved me in that way. I'll call them "Mom's Investments" because they describe the ways my mother invested her love, and God's love, in me.

2. **We can give *freely* because we have freely received.**

"Freely you have received, freely give" (Matthew 10:8).

The One Anothers are to be given freely; we should never give with the expectation of remuneration. Obviously, this would include monetary exchange ("I'll accept you if you pay me five hundred dollars." "I'll comfort you in exchange for your car."), but it also means that our giving should never be based on any expectation of return. ("I'll forgive you if you will forget my credit card purchases." "I'll prefer you today if you'll prefer me tomorrow." "I'll accept you if you'll vote for me.")

A cartoon showed a singer about to perform in church. He addressed the audience, "I'd like to share a song with you that the Lord gave me a year ago … and even though he did give it to me, any reproduction of this song in any form without my written consent will constitute infringement of copyright laws which grants me the right to sue [you] … praise God."[2]

We never pay for what we receive from God, so we must not charge for what we give or take credit for it. Give freely.

3. **We can give *generously* because we have generously received.**

"The grace of our Lord was poured out on me abundantly" (1 Timothy 1:14).

God is not stingy, and neither should we be. He does not dispense his grace in small quantities, and neither should we.

We may erroneously think that God's divine commodities are limited; therefore we have to ration them out. This mentality could cause us subconsciously to think, *I only have four ounces of comfort to distribute per month, so I better be careful to make it last.* To the contrary, we have an unlimited supply of comfort—a carte blanche. Dispense an enormous amount of comfort every day, and your supply will not diminish in the least. Give love generously because you'll never run out. The apostle John commented on the abundance of God's provision when he wrote, "How great is the love the Father has lavished on us" (1 John 3:1).

Interestingly, we cannot fully comprehend all that God has given to us until we begin to give to others. In Philemon 6, the apostle Paul said, "I pray that you may be active in sharing your faith, so that you will have a full understanding of every good thing we have in Christ."

4. **We must give *indiscriminately.***

"My brothers, as believers in our glorious Lord Jesus Christ, don't show favoritism" (James 2:1).

When God poured out his love, he didn't pick and choose upon whom it would fall; he loved the entire world. In like manner, as we dispense his love, we must not show favoritism.

To avoid showing favoritism, we need to remember two things:

Give all of the One Anothers to everyone; don't be selective in which ones you give. Don't have the attitude that says, "I'll greet you, but I'm not going to accept you. I'll admonish you, but I'm not going to encourage you. I'm willing to show you support, but not preference." Minister *all* of the One Anothers to every person.

Give all of the One Anothers to all people, yes, even to your enemies. In other words, we can't have the attitude that says, "I'll comfort my children, but not my spouse. I'll accept people who look like me, but not anyone who is different. I'll encourage fellow Christians, but not unbelievers." We must be willing to minister all of the One Anothers to *all* people. Otherwise we show favoritism, which the Bible prohibits (1 Timothy 5:21). For sure, some people are more difficult to love than others, but that challenge may be the "litmus test" of whether or not we truly love as Christ loved us. "You have heard that it was said, 'Love your neighbor and hate your enemy.' But I tell you: Love your enemies. … If you love those who love you, what reward will you get? … Do not even pagans do that?" (Matthew 5:43–47).

In short, "Give all to all."

… during Jesus' three years of earthly ministry, he basically just performed the One Anothers.
The Bible says he went about "doing good."
What good did he do? *The One Anothers.*
HE SHOWED THE WORLD HOW LOVE BEHAVES.

---

5. **It is more enjoyable to give than to receive.**

"The Lord Jesus himself said: 'It is more blessed to give than to receive.'" (Acts 20:35).

I once heard that when author Thomas Carlyle was a boy, a beggar came to the front door of his house. His parents were out, and he was alone. On a boyish impulse, he broke into his own savings bank and gave the beggar all that was in it. He tells us that never before or since did he know such sheer happiness as came to him in that moment.

There is indeed joy in giving.

We struggle so much with selfishness that it often takes many years to discover that giving really is more satisfying than receiving. Many never learn this lesson. In faith, we should accept this advice because it comes from the greatest philanthropist of all time—Jesus Christ.

Write about a time when you experienced the joy of giving.

_____

_____

_____

6. **We are to relate to one another in the same way God has related to (loved) us.**

"As I have loved you, so you must love one another" (John 13:34).

Jesus described the 11th Commandment as a *new* commandment. The command to "love others" was not new because part of the Jewish law was to "love your neighbor as yourself" (Leviticus 19:18). It was the qualification to "love others *as I have loved you*" that was so radical. During his earthly ministry, Jesus redefined love, or better said, he accurately and thoroughly defined love for the first time. It's not that Christ raised the bar so high that we could not participate; he actually made the message of love so plain that we could not claim ignorance. He simply said, "Do to others as I have done to you." What makes this a tough assignment is the fact that his love is unconditional, unmerited, and unceasing.

> In commanding us to love others, God is not asking us to do something that he has not already done. He is not asking us to give to others anything that he has not already given to us.

I am convinced that during Jesus' three years of earthly ministry, he basically just performed the One Anothers. The Bible says he went about "doing good" (Acts 10:38). What good did he do? The One Anothers. He showed the world how love behaves. How prolific was his ministry? If the many things Jesus did were all written down, "even the whole world would not have room for the books that would be written" (John 21:25).

And how did Jesus train his disciples? Initially, he called them just to "be with him" (Mark 3:14). In essence, he said, "Come hang out with me for three years. You don't have to *do* a lot. Just observe and listen. Soak it in. Then there will come a time for *you* to do something." Their curriculum simply consisted of hearing Jesus teach truth and then observing him demonstrating love. So for thirty-six months, day after day, they witnessed him ministering the One Anothers to other people. They also experienced firsthand his ministry of the One Anothers to them as individuals.

It's important to note that Jesus proclaimed the 11th Commandment at the *end* of his three-year ministry, not at the beginning. Just hours before his death, Jesus said, "Love one another *as I have loved you*." Basically, he was saying, "What you have seen me do for others and for you, go and do likewise." In response to this statement, Simon Peter might have thought, *I remember when Jesus spoke encouraging words to the condemned, adulterous woman. I also recall his ministry of encouragement to my family and me when my mother-in-law was sick. I saw him love others through the ministry of encouragement, and I felt loved by his encouraging words and deeds. I know what he's talking about! I can do that!*

Likewise, although the disciples were shocked at Jesus' acceptance of the Samaritan woman (John 4:27 says they "were surprised to find him talking with a woman"), they must have been deeply stirred when they noticed the profound impact it had on her life and others. "Many of the Samaritans from that town believed in him because of the woman's testimony" (John 4:39). But the powerful ministry of acceptance was really driven home when, through the course of three years, the disciples realized that Jesus accepted *them* just the way they were, with all their flaws and inconsistencies. The disciples themselves were a shady group—uneducated fishermen, a tax collector, a betrayer—men of fear and unbelief. And yet Jesus continually looked beyond their imperfections, accepted them as they were, and continued to love them deeply.

In commanding us to love others, God is not asking us to do something that he has not already done. He is not asking us to give to others anything that he has not already given to us.

It's interesting to note that throughout the thirty-three years of Jesus' earthly life, he was simply sharing with the world the love that he was constantly receiving from his Father. "As the Father has loved me, so have I loved you" (John 15:9).

7. When we minister the One Anothers to other people, we are ministering to Christ.

"God is not unjust; he will not forget your work and the love you have shown him as you have helped his people and continue to help them" (Hebrews 6:10).

Tony Campolo tells the true story of a Jewish boy who suffered under the Nazis in World War II. He was living in a small Polish village when he and all the other Jews of the vicinity were rounded up by Nazi SS troops and sentenced to death. This boy joined his neighbors in digging a shallow ditch for their graves and then faced the firing squad with his parents. Sprayed with machine-gun fire, bodies fell into the ditch, and the Nazis covered the crumpled bodies with dirt. But none of the bullets hit the little boy. He was splattered with the blood of his parents, and when they fell into the ditch, he pretended to be dead and fell on top of them. The grave was so shallow that the thin covering of dirt did not prevent air from getting through to him so that he could breathe.

When we minister the One Anothers to other people, we are ministering to Christ.

Several hours later, when darkness fell, he clawed his way out of the grave. With blood and dirt caked to his little body, he made his way to the nearest house and begged for help. Recognizing him as one of the Jewish boys marked for death, he was turned away at house after house as people feared trouble from the SS troops. Then something inside seemed to guide him to say something that was very strange for a Jewish boy to say. When the next family responded to his timid knocking in the still of the night, they heard him cry, "Don't you recognize me? I am the Jesus you say you love." After a pause, the woman who stood in the doorway swept him into her arms and kissed him. From that day on, the members of that family cared for that boy as though he was one of their own.[3]

When we love others, in a sense, we are loving Christ. And when we minister to others, we are somehow actually ministering to Christ (Matthew 25:31–40). This mystery is based on the fact that we are the body of Christ. To love one another is to love Christ, and to neglect or harm one another is to neglect or harm Christ (Acts 9:4).

It's been said that the only way to serve God is to do something for someone else. "Whatever you did for one of the least of these brothers of mine, you did for me" (Matthew 25:40). Our debt to God is payable to man.

8. When we minister the One Anothers, we are dispensing God's "glorious riches."

"God will meet all your needs according to his glorious riches in Christ Jesus" (Philippians 4:19).

Have you heard about the kid who, having grown up in church, held the firm conviction that Jesus was left-handed? When asked to explain his position, he confidently responded, "Jesus is left-handed because the Bible says that he's seated on his right hand."

A slight misunderstanding of Ephesians 1:20.

When I was a kid, I had my own set of misunderstandings. One of them was Philippians 4:19. In the late '50s, we used the King James Version of the Bible, so the verse read, "My God shall supply all your needs according to his riches in glory."

Being a visual person, I composed, in my mind, a picture of what this verse must look like, starting at the end of the verse and working forward.

- "In glory"—this must mean "in heaven" because we often sang the song, "There's a New Name Written Down in Glory," and the lyrics referred to heaven.
- "Riches"—that must mean money, and in my mind, gold.

So God has this huge slab of gold up in heaven, located inside a huge vault (my child's perspective didn't figure that vaults would be unnecessary in heaven). Whenever I had a need (my only concept of need was physical and financial), God would take a cheese slicer (Mom had just bought one), slice off a thin piece of gold, and drop it down from heaven. I never thought through how the gold would be converted into usable currency.

And that's how God would meet needs according to his riches in glory.

Thirty years later . . .

My mother passed away a year ago January. She was a good and godly woman. Several nights ago, I dreamed I was walking through our old home. As I entered each room, Mom was there. In the den, she was sitting on the couch reading the Bible. In the kitchen, she was cooking eggs and cinnamon toast. In the dining room, she was serving dinner. In my dream, I wept through every room. I woke up crying.

Later in the morning, my teenage daughter, sensing my sadness, asked me how I was doing. After I told her about the dream, she reached out, held my hand, and said, "Dad, I know you miss Grandma a lot. I'm very sorry you had such a sad dream. It hurts me to think of you waking up crying. I love you."

I was comforted.

On another occasion, I was struggling with feelings of inadequacy mixed with feelings of ambiguity about the direction of my ministry. I felt as low as the proverbial cockroach in a crawl space. My friend John just happened to call to see if we could have lunch. After eating, we stopped by the church for a time of prayer in the chapel. He shared, "Don, your ministry has touched so many people. Just last week a friend of mine mentioned how deeply you have impacted his life. You are loved and appreciated by many people—including me."

I was encouraged.

For nine months, I flew every weekend from Dallas to Florida to do interim work at a church in Ft. Lauderdale. During the week my full-time ministry would often have me on the road as well. The up-side of this busy schedule was that the ministry opportunities were being blessed, and I racked up enough frequent-flier miles to go to the moon and back—and take my family. The downside was that my wife and daughters were beginning to feel neglected. My wife shared, "Sweetheart, the girls and I really miss you. We need you to be at home more."

I was admonished.

I was reminiscing with my wife one evening about our early days of marriage. Mary shared a painful incident that I had forgotten. During the third year we were married, Mary's father, who was living in another city, became seriously ill. One Sunday afternoon, we received a call from a hospital where Mary's father was in serious condition. They told us they would call back if his condition worsened. Mary reminded me that I went to church that evening to perform my pastoral duties and left her alone. During the time I was gone, she was afraid that the hospital would call and say that her father had died. Fortunately, he did not die that evening, but the damage was done. It hurt Mary deeply that I prioritized my ministry over her.

As Mary shared, a sense of sorrow and regret came over me. I had hurt my wife seventeen years ago and had never made it right. I asked Mary to forgive me. She reached over, took me by the hand, and said, "Don, I forgive you."

I was forgiven.

When I was recently reading through Philippians, I once again encountered chapter 4, verse 19. I was reading in the New International Version, which says, "My God will meet all your needs according to his glorious riches in Christ Jesus." Because of life's journey, I had a clearer understanding of what that verse really means. I realized that the "riches" of Philippians 4:19 are not hay, wood, and stubble, which will be consumed in a millisecond at the Lord's coming (1 Corinthians 3:12–15); they are non-material in nature. I believe that the "riches" of Christ Jesus are the One Anothers. By allowing us to distribute the One Anothers, God allows us to be stewards of his "glorious riches." What an honor.

And that's the essence of the 11th Commandment. We need to learn how to receive and distribute his glorious riches; we need to learn how to love and be loved.

That sets the agenda for our time together, and it also determines the structure of this workbook.

In this workbook, I've selected eight of the One Anothers that seem to be prioritized throughout Scripture to study in detail. In the last chapter, we'll briefly discuss eight others. By the time you finish this workbook, you'll be equipped with the practical skills of how to love others in sixteen different ways.

Recruiting Helpers

In order to benefit the most from this study, I encourage you to identify three different people who will help you in your journey.

A Secret Recipient

Think of a person with whom you interact daily, someone with whom who you would enjoy sharing the One Anothers. It's important that you *do not* tell this person that you are studying the One Anothers, and *do not* tell this person that he or she is your "secret project." Week by week, you are going to "experiment" on this person by ministering to him or her the particular One Another being studied. In a loving way, this person will be your "guinea pig." This may sound a bit sly and underhanded, and if we were experimenting with mind-altering drugs, I wouldn't ask for the cloak of secrecy. But you'll actually be blessing this individual. Your assignment will be to encourage, accept, greet, comfort, forgive, support, and prefer this person. You'll be like the anonymous benefactor in Charles Dickens' novel *Great Expectations*. You'll be Mr. Magwitch; your friend will be Pip.

The approach is:

- Don't tell your friend that you are engaged in this study.
- Each week, as we study a different One Another, begin ministering that particular One Another to your friend and continue to do so … forever.

Person's name: _____

A Secret Recipient Who May Not Know Christ

I sincerely believe that the One Anothers are the key to effective evangelism. As we minister God's love to people, they will be deeply touched and drawn to the source of so great a love.

Therefore, the second person I want you to identify is someone who may not know Jesus as Savior, and someone to whom you would enjoy ministering the One Anothers. Take the same approach with this person as with your other secret recipient: Don't relate your strategy; just administer love. I would encourage you, *initially*, not to share the gospel message with this person. That is, don't witness to or confront your friend with the claims of Christ, but rather simply inundate him or her with the love of Christ. Of course, you'll want to be sensitive to the Holy Spirit's leading; the Spirit may indeed have you share the gospel message immediately, and if so, certainly obey.

This strategy is based on the last phrase of the 11th Commandment: "All men will know that you are my disciples, if you love one another" (John 13:35). Is it possible that people can recognize our Christianity not by what we *say,* but by how we *love?* Is it possible that they might be more receptive to the *claims of Christ* after they have experienced firsthand the *love of Christ?*

It is similar to the strategy that Peter gives to wives who have unbelieving husbands: "Wives, in the same way be submissive to your husbands so that, if any of them do not believe the word, they may be won over without words by the behavior of their wives" (1 Peter 3:1).

In time, there will be an ideal opportunity for sharing with this person how he or she can have a personal relationship with Christ. But begin by simply loving this person.

It would be best to choose someone you see regularly, even daily. It will be difficult to regularly share the One Anothers with someone whom you see infrequently.

Person's name: _____

Will this person recognize that you are a Christian,

not just because you say you are

but because she sees the ministry of Christ flowing through you?

A One Another Partner

Throughout this study you'll need an "OA partner." This is someone:

- whom you know well and see often,
- whom you will also "experiment" on,
- who will give you feedback, and
- with whom you will share the truths you are learning.

For instance, after studying "encourage one another," you'll meet with your OA partner, share what you've learned, ask him or her to evaluate your current ministry of encouragement, and commit that you want to be an encouragement to him or her. You'll ask this person to "grade you" on your progress in the area of encouragement for as long as the course lasts (and perhaps beyond). By the end of this study, your OA partner will be observing your life in eight key areas (the eight One Anothers we'll study in detail).

May I suggest who this person might be? If you are married, your spouse would be ideal, even if he or she is taking this course. If you are a parent, you might want to choose one of your children. Of course, the idea is that, hopefully, we'll learn to share these One Anothers with everyone with whom we come in contact. But it will be helpful to have one person to focus on who will give us feedback.

Initially, you'll need to meet with this person to explain the project and to solicit his involvement. The time commitment will be about thirty minutes per lesson.

OA partner's name: _____

Before continuing, let me encourage you to take the above assignment seriously. The goal of this study is to help bring about a significant change in your life as to how you relate to others. It would be sad indeed for you to complete this entire study and gain only a mental understanding of these spiritual truths without actually having the truth affect your life. If that happens, you'll suffer from the malady described in 1 Corinthians 8:1: "Knowledge puffs up, but love builds up." Most Christians don't need more knowledge; we need to learn practical and consistent love.

For this to happen, we need a measure of accountability. It's been said, "People don't do what you expect; they do what you inspect." And that's why I've asked you to select three people and to relate to them intentionally throughout this study.

- Relative to your "secret recipient"—Will ministering the One Anothers to a person really minister grace to him? Will it make a difference in his life? Will it enhance your relationship with him? Will you sense the personal joy of genuinely loving this person?

- Relative to your unbelieving "secret recipient"—Will this person recognize that you are a Christian, not just because you say you are but because she sees the ministry of Christ flowing through you? Will your love cause her to be inquisitive about the love of Christ, possibly laying the groundwork for a relationship with Christ?

- Relative to your "OA partner"—Are you willing to vulnerably ask, "Am I an encouraging person? Do I encourage you as often as I should?" Are you willing to be accountable for the truth you'll be learning by saying, "Over the next several weeks, I'm going to try to incorporate the ministry of encouragement in my life. Please tell me how I'm doing"? Are you willing to share what you are learning by asking, "Can I take twenty minutes to share with you what I have learned about the ministry of encouragement?"

These three people will play an important role in your life throughout this course. If you're serious about making the most of this study, identify these three people and commit to love them.

Practical Suggestions and Powerful Results

We need to discuss one more thing before beginning our study. There are eight "Practical Suggestions" relative to ministering the One Anothers that are foundational in nature and applicable to all the One Anothers. These are the "nuts and bolts" of the system.

In addition, there are seven "Powerful Results" that you can anticipate happening because of your ministering the One Anothers. In other words, what are the end results of ministering the One Anothers? What can you expect to happen as a result of this ministry?

So I have eight suggestions and seven results to share. But I don't want to share them all at once. Discussing them all up front might bog us down, and I want to start studying the specific One Anothers as quickly as possible. Therefore, I'll share one Practical Suggestion and one Powerful Result at the end of each of the next eight chapters.

Remember though, although they are placed at the end of a particular chapter in which we have studied a particular One Another, these suggestions and results apply to all of the One Anothers

Group Time—Session One

Each member of the group should give his or her individual response to the first four questions. Allow about two minutes for each person's response.

1. What was the most interesting concept in this chapter?
2. Who will your secret recipient be? Your unchurched secret recipient? Your OA partner?
3. Refer back to page 1. Share the name of the person you feel has loved you the most and what that person did to make you feel loved.
4. Share your responses on pages 6, 7, 8 & 10.

As a group, discuss the following issues:
    a. Discuss this statement, "Don't keep telling me, 'I love you' without demonstrating your love to me."
    b. Discuss this statement, "Assurance of love is needed daily."

Homework:
1. Review chapter 1 and complete all fill-in-the-blank sections.
2. Read and process chapter 2.

PREFER ONE ANOTHER

"In honor [give] preference to one another" (Romans 12:10 NKJV).

In *A Tale of Two Cities, Charles Dickens* presents a classic illustration of John 15:13. In fact, Dickens quotes this verse in his book. Two men, Charles Darnay and Sydney Carton, have become best friends. Darnay is a young Frenchman who is thrown in a dungeon and will face the guillotine the next morning. Carton is a wasted lawyer who has finished his life, as it were, as a loose-living individual living in England. Carton hears of Darnay's imprisonment and, through a chain of events, gets into the dungeon and changes garments with Darnay, who escapes. The next morning Sydney Carton makes his way up the steps that lead to the guillotine. Dickens writes, "Greater love has no one than this, than one lay down his life for his friend."[1]

Dickens's story is, of course, a human illustration of the divine exchange that took place when Christ preferred us by offering to pay the penalty for our sin. Christ's profound act of preferring others is described in Philippians 2:1–11. The most challenging part of this Scripture passage is verse 5: "Your attitude should be the same as that of Christ Jesus." He preferred us, so we should prefer others.

The Foundational One Another

Prefer One Another is the foundational One Another; all others are dependent upon it. Preferring others is the *attitude* that motivates us to want to *do* the One Anothers. If I'm not willing to prefer you, I'll be reluctant to encourage you, to support you, or to comfort you because ministering the One Anothers requires focusing on others instead of ourselves. We must concentrate on giving instead of receiving.

While preferring others will inevitably lead to certain acts, it begins as an attitude.

The Greatest Hindrance to Preferring Others

The story is told of a mother who was preparing pancakes for her sons, Kevin, age five, and Ryan, age three. The boys began to argue over who would get the first pancake. Their mother saw the opportunity for a moral lesson. "If Jesus were sitting here, he would say, 'Let my brother have the first pancake. I can wait.'" Kevin turned to his younger brother and said, "Ryan, you be Jesus."

We expect children to be selfish. Part of the maturation process involves teaching children how to share and consider others. But some of us, even as adults, still struggle with considering others more important than ourselves. The biggest hindrance to preferring others is selfishness. As long as we're focused on ourselves, other people will not be a concern or a priority.

James 3:16 indicates that selfishness is a root sin that leads to many other problems: "For where you have envy and selfish ambition, there you find disorder and every evil practice." If preferring others is, indeed, the foundational One Another, then selfish ambition will prevent us from engaging in any of the One Anothers. Perhaps this neglect is what James refers to as "every evil practice." We must learn to focus our attention on others, becoming other-people-oriented instead of self-oriented.

Dying to Self

Preferring others often requires dying to self. Perhaps that's why the apostle Paul shared, "I die every day" (1 Corinthians 15:31). When our personal preferences are different from someone else's personal preferences, we are obliged to show deference to others. For instance, consider this situation: You want to play golf on Saturday, but your spouse wants to visit relatives. In order to prefer your spouse, you'll have to die to your desire to play golf.

> In order to be free to prefer others, we need a healthy self-image and a proper appreciation of who we are as individuals. It's hard to focus on others unless we are secure in who we are.

A friend of mine shared with me that, for the entire week, he had looked forward to fishing on the weekend. When Saturday came, he got up before dawn, hooked up his boat, and went to the lake. It was a beautiful morning. He knew the best place to fish was on the other side of the lake and that the best time to fish was just before dawn, so he had timed it just right—a twenty-minute boat ride across the lake would put him at the right place at just the right time. About halfway across the lake, he noticed a man in a boat who was trying to get his attention. Sure enough, the guy's engine had conked out. He asked my friend, "Will you please tow me back to the dock?" My friend quickly calculated the slow trip to the dock and then back across the lake to his favorite fishing hole. He wouldn't be able to make it in time. But remembering the admonition to prefer one another, he swallowed hard, died to self, and said yes. My friend lived out the admonition of 1 John 3:16: "This is how we know what love is: Jesus Christ laid down his life for us. And we ought to lay down our lives for our brothers."

However, preferring others does not mean we must abdicate who we are, our importance as a human being, or what we can contribute to any situation; nor does preferring others require that we allow others to dominate us. Preferring others does not mean we become a doormat. There must be a balance. Preferring others, if taken to an extreme, will allow others to abuse us. If you're part of a relationship in which you continually prefer the other person but are never being preferred, there is nothing wrong in engaging in another of the One Anothers—Admonish One Another. In a nice way, it would be appropriate to share, "It seems like our relationship may be out of balance. I feel like I'm always preferring you, but you never prefer me."

Enjoying a Healthy Self-Image

In order to be free to prefer others, we need a healthy self-image and a proper appreciation of who we are as individuals. It's hard to focus on others unless we are secure in who we are.

There's an interesting anecdote from the life of Jesus that illustrates this point. As a part of the Upper Room experience, Jesus washed his disciples' feet. John gives us insight into the thoughts of Jesus prior to this grand demonstration of serving and preferring his disciples: "Jesus knew that the Father had put all things under his power, and that he had come from God and was returning to God; so he got up from the meal, took off his outer clothing, and wrapped a towel around his waist. After that, he poured water into a basin and began to wash his disciples' feet" (John 13:3–5).

Notice Jesus' frame of mind prior to the foot washing. Jesus was confident in who he was, comfortable in his relationship with his Father, and secure in his future. In this state of mind, he preferred and served others. He even preferred and served Judas, who would soon betray him.

It's interesting to note that in this particular Scripture passage, another One Another is mentioned "Now that I, your Lord and teacher, have washed your feet, you also *should wash one another's feet* (verse 14; emphasis added). In order to do what Jesus did, we must first think as he thought and feel as he felt.

To be free to prefer and serve others, we must understand who we are in Christ.

- As we become confident that God will meet all our needs, we will be able to focus on meeting other people's needs.
- As we become confident in who we are in Christ, we won't have to "prove ourselves" to others but can serve them.
- As we realize that our future is secure, we will be less inclined to worry about our personal assets and will freely give to others.

With which areas of self-esteem do you struggle? How might this impede your willingness and ability to prefer others?

_____

_____

The Reward

The Bible indicates that there is a reward for preferring others. Although this should not be the motivating factor behind our preferring others, it is a by-product. For instance, the description in Philippians 2 of how Jesus preferred us ends with this thought: "Therefore God exalted him to the highest place" (v. 9). Likewise, James 4:10 says, "Humble yourselves before the Lord [humility is the key attitude in preferring others], and he will lift you up."

Practical Ways to Prefer One Another

1. Take the initiative to discover other people's needs, interests and preferences.

For instance:
- I know my spouse has a deep need for respect (or security, comfort, etc.).
- I know my son enjoys playing basketball in the backyard.
- I know my boss likes for me to maintain a clean and organized office.
- I know my coworker likes Mexican food.
- I know my mother's favorite way to relax on Saturday is to sleep late and then to eat a leisurely breakfast.

It will be difficult to prefer others if we don't know what they prefer.

People will be particularly blessed when we take the initiative to discover their preferences instead of having to be told.

Consider the following exchange:

> Bob: "Let's go eat Mexican food for lunch today."
> Jim: "I'd love to; it's my favorite type of food."
> Bob: "I thought so."
> Jim: "How do you know that?"
> Bob: "The other day when your wife called to see if you had left the office, I asked her."

Write down some needs and preferences of your—

Secret recipient: _____

Unchurched secret recipient: _____

One Another partner: _____

2. **Discern people's skills, talents, and gifts, and initiate opportunities for them to use them.**

    - Susan enjoys singing solos. Let's ask her to sing at the banquet.
    - Robert really enjoys golf. Let's ask him to serve on the golf tournament committee.
    - Sarah has a knack for theater. Let's find a community theater where she could perform.

3. **Learn to prefer others in various ways:**

    Prefer other people's—

    - Emotional states—"I want to go to the movie tonight, but I know my spouse has had a rough day and would rather stay home."
    - Preferences—"I know you want to go to the beach for our vacation, so let's plan to go."
    - Needs—"I know you need to be comforted."

4. **When in a group of people, make an effort to include everyone in the conversation.**

    In a group setting, it's not uncommon for two or three extroverts to dominate the conversation unless a conscientious effort is made to include everyone. Some people (perhaps they are shy or perhaps they are simply preferring others) will not aggressively engage in a group conversation unless given the opportunity to do so. Encourage everyone to talk by asking group questions, such as "Let's all share what we did over the Labor Day holiday," and then giving everyone a chance to answer.

5. **Become other-people-oriented instead of self-oriented.**

    Have you ever thought about how self-oriented we all are? In the course of everyday living, we tend to see each person and situation only as it relates to us. When entering a crowded room, our natural instinct is to wonder what others are thinking about us: *I wonder if he heard about my promotion. Can she tell that I dyed my hair?* We even view world events through the lens of how they will affect us: *I hope the crisis in Western Europe won't affect my upcoming vacation. –The Robertsons, four houses down, sold their house for a very low price, which probably devalues my home quite a bit. – My supervisor was fired. Aha! Finally, that promotion!*

For thousands of years, humans thought that all the planets of the solar system revolved around the earth. After all, we live on it. In like manner, we often think that the rest of the world revolves around our lives and that everyone should be caught up in our orbit. We tend to be self-oriented, but we need to become other-people-oriented.

For instance, when you wake up tomorrow, instead of thinking about what your day will look like, consider what your friend's day will involve. Instead of concentrating on how you feel, consider how your spouse is feeling. If you have a friend or loved one living in another city, think about what the weather is like where he or she is.

For thousands of years, humans thought that all the planets of the solar system revolved around the earth. After all, we live on it. In like manner,

we often think that the rest of the world

revolves around our lives

and that everyone should be caught up in our orbit.

Enter someone else's world for a while; rotate in his or her orbit.

A good indication of our willingness to prefer others can be seen in our willingness to observe others—to use all five senses to detect their desires, attitudes, emotional conditions, comfort levels, and opinions.

My family and I live in the Dallas/Ft. Worth metroplex. One evening when we were at home, the weather became quite severe—thunderstorms and tornados. During the storm, one of our church members called on behalf of her nine-year-old daughter. They were watching the weather report on television and noticed that the storm was particularly acute in our part of town (they live on the other side of the city). The young girl was concerned for our safety and asked her mother to call and see if we were all right.

I was extremely blessed to know that someone was thinking about us. But I was quite taken aback that a nine-year-old would be so unselfish as to consider the well-being of someone other than herself. I would argue that her "not looking to her own interests, but also to the interests of others" was a powerful testimony to her emotional and spiritual maturity. It was a significant event indicating that at an early age she was becoming other-people-oriented.

6. **Be a good listener who encourages people to talk about themselves.**

Preferring others will impact our conversations; we'll be more inclined to listen than talk. Our attitude will be, "I would rather listen to you—to hear your thoughts and learn more about you—than to have you listen to me." In any given conversation, if we talk more than 50 percent of the time, chances are we're not showing preference to the other person.

Elizabeth Chevalier, author of the best-selling novel, *Driven Women*, wrote in a letter to Macmillan, "Have you heard the one about the novelist who met an old friend? After they had talked for two hours, the novelist said, 'Now we've talked about me long enough—let's talk about you! What did you think of my last novel?'"

I had a similar encounter several years ago when my wife and I went to a Fourth of July party. I decided to try to get to know the host a little better, so he and I sat on the couch, and I initiated a conversation. He talked constantly for thirty minutes; I didn't say more than a few sentences. But not only did he talk the whole time, he talked about himself, not once asking about me. He didn't ask what I did for a living or about my family. He was completely self-absorbed.

Not only is it important not to dominate conversations, it's also important to encourage people to talk about themselves. William E. Gladstone, the distinguished British statesman, took a woman to dinner one night. The next evening, she dined next to Benjamin Disraeli, his equally distinguished opponent. When asked her opinion of the two men, she replied thoughtfully, "When I left the dining room after sitting with Mr. Gladstone, I thought he was the cleverest man in England. But after sitting next to Mr. Disraeli, I thought I was the cleverest woman in England."

Our conversations should focus on others.

Mom's Investment

■ My mother was a simple, godly woman. She and Dad lived a modest lifestyle and, while she was of average intelligence, she was naive to the ways of the world. She did have a deep-rooted faith in God and his Word. She didn't understand Greek or Hebrew and would graciously avoid conversations involving higher criticism or theological debate, but she was the most Christ-like person I have known. She lived the One Anothers. ■ One particular anecdote, which occurred just days before she died, was particularly representative of her life, which was devoted to loving others. It was "vintage Mom." Her pastor told us the story at her funeral. ■ Several days before mom died, he went to visit her in the hospital. Her health had deteriorated such that she only weighed seventy-seven pounds. She was being fed intravenously because her jaw was almost immobile. ■ When Mom heard the hospital door swing open and recognized her visitor as her pastor, she began to mumble something. In an attempt to hear what she was saying, the pastor bent over the bed, putting his ear only inches away from Mom's mouth. ■ She was asking, "Have you had dinner yet?" ■ That was Mom. Though slowly wasting away herself, she was concerned that her minister might not have eaten dinner. In her heart, I suppose she was prepared to cook him a feast. To her dying breath, she preferred others. ■ Mom has given me a tremendous heritage to live up to. In the midst of my teaching conferences, writing books, and other venues of public ministry, I hope I'll not neglect the pure, unadulterated ministry my mother taught by example and lived consistently all her life. It was the same attitude that Christ had: "Each of you should look not only to your own interests but also to the interests of others" (Philippians 2:4).

Write your own definition of Prefer One Another.

_____

_____

_____

Personal Journal

1. Write about a time in your life when someone preferred you. _____

_____

2. Write about the last time you preferred someone else. _____

_____

3. Write about a time when you observed someone else preferring others. _____

_____

4. There's nothing wrong with having definitive opinions and preferences, and there's nothing wrong with sharing them with others. Preferring others doesn't mean that we cannot share these personal opinions and preferences. But when we are described as "opinionated," it usually means we're being too forthright, aggressive, or stubborn with our opinions; we're defending and holding on to our opinions. This is not good. Do people consider you to be opinionated? Stubborn?

    My opinion: _____

    My OA partner's opinion: _____

5. Part of preferring others involves being a good listener and talking less (see James 1:19). Are you a good listener? Do you talk too much?

    My opinion: _____

    My OA partner's opinion: _____

6. What can you do this week to prefer your two secret recipients?

    Secret recipient: _____

    Unchurched secret recipient: _____

7. On a scale from 1 to 10 (1 being, "I need to greatly improve" and 10 being, "I do a good job"), how well do you prefer others? Ask your OA Partner to rate you.

    I rated myself a _____.

    My OA partner rated me a _____.

Practical Suggestion #1

There is a particular sequence for the successful distribution of the One Anothers. Three of them need to occur successively, after which there is no particular order.

Step One—Prefer One Another

As previously mentioned, Prefer One Another is the foundational One Another. All others are dependent upon it. Preferring others is the *attitude* that motivates us to want to *do* the One Anothers. Ministering the One Anothers requires focusing on others instead of ourselves; we must concentrate on giving instead of receiving.

Preferring others begins as an attitude. It's the same attitude that Christ had as described in Philippians 2—one of sacrifice. Philippians 2:1–7 is a very significant Scripture passage because it reveals the heart attitude of Jesus that prompted his incarnation. Let's take a closer look at this passage.

In verses 1–2, Paul mentions some of the One Anothers: "If you have any *encouragement* from being united with Christ, if any *comfort* from his love, if any *fellowship* with the Spirit, if any *tenderness* and *compassion*, then make my joy complete by being like-minded" (emphasis added).

In verses 3–4, he presents the basic principle—Prefer One Another. "Do nothing out of selfish ambition or vain conceit, but in humility consider others better than yourselves. Each of you should look not only to your own interests, but also to the interests of others."

In verses 5–7, he presents Jesus as the prime example of preferring others: "Your attitude should be the same as that of Christ Jesus: Who, being in very nature God, did not consider equality with God something to be grasped, but made himself nothing, taking the very nature of a servant, being made in human likeness."

Christ's willingness to prefer us (he looked to our interests, not his own) is what motivated him to leave his world and to enter into ours. An attitude (Prefer One Another) prompted an action (he left his world and entered into ours); both were precursors to the other One Anothers.

Step Two—Accept One Another

Once we are willing to prefer others, we must then be willing to accept them. In chapter 3 we'll discuss acceptance in detail, but for now let's use this simple expression, "By accepting you I affirm that you are created in the image of God and that in his creative splendor he has created you unique. I receive you just the way you are. I will never withhold giving any of the One Anothers to you. I will not prefer one person over another because all humans are of equal value."

It's easy to see how a lack of acceptance will impede ministering the One Anothers:

- I don't like the color of your skin, so I'm hesitant to greet you.
- I come from a different socio-economic background than you, so I'm reluctant to encourage you.
- Your theology is different from mine, so I'm hesitant to be kind to you.
- You have long hair, so I'm reticent about comforting you.

While few of us would actually verbalize such bias, most of us struggle with inward, prejudicial thoughts that invariably affect how we relate to others.

Before the apostle Peter could become all that God wanted him to be, God had to press upon his heart the necessity of accepting others. Having been raised in the Jewish tradition, Peter could not fathom the possibility that God's grace could be extended to the Gentiles. So God had to give him a potent lesson on Accept One Another. It is recorded in Acts 10.

During his afternoon prayer time, Peter fell into a trance. He saw heaven opened and a large sheet being let down which contained all kinds of four-footed animals. The Lord said, "Peter, eat"—to which Peter replied, "Surely not, Lord! I have never eaten anything impure or unclean." The vision occurred three times. While Peter was wondering about what the vision might mean, three men came to his house to ask him to visit Cornelius, who was a Gentile. The Lord said, "Do not hesitate to go with them, for I have sent them." Peter went and shared the message of the gospel with Cornelius and his household, and they received the message of Christ. Indeed, the gospel message was for everyone. Peter summarized what he learned by saying, "I now realize how true it is that God does not show favoritism but accepts men from every nation who fear him and do what is right" (vv. 34–35).

Peter's initial unwillingness to accept the Gentiles prevented him from ministering to them. Likewise, our unwillingness to accept someone will impede our ministry to him.

If the One Anothers are to flow freely and uninhibitedly from our lives, we must unreservedly accept all people.

Step Three—Greet One Another

With a desire to prefer others and a willingness to accept everyone, we are now prepared to take the next step—Greet One Another.

Greeting others is the front door, the entryway to the other One Anothers. It is the first initiative.

The initial, divine greeting is recorded in John 1:14: "The Word became flesh and made his dwelling among us." Motivated by a desire to prefer us and a willingness to accept us, God entered into our world—he greeted us.

In chapter 4, we'll study Greet One Another in detail. One of the things we'll learn is that this particular One Another doesn't take long to "perform"—usually only a few seconds; then we segue into one of the other One Anothers. But it makes sense that greeting must come first. How will I know which One Another you may need at any particular moment if I don't first enter into your world and make contact?

So the order of these three One Anothers is important.

- I will be unable to minister the One Anothers to you unless I *greet* you.
- I will be reluctant to *greet* you if I'm not willing to *accept* you.
- I will be hesitant to *accept* you if I'm not willing to *prefer* you.
- I will be disinclined to *prefer* you if I don't *love* you.

This order is reflected in the structure of this workbook. Chapters 2, 3, and 4 discuss Prefer One Another, Accept One Another, and Greet One Another, in that order.

Powerful Result #1

Because the One Anothers require us to focus on others, ministering them will help us overcome a serious spiritual malady—selfishness.

A small boy and his sister were riding on the back of the new wooden horse given to them as a present. Suddenly the boy turned to his sister and said, "If one of us would get off, there would be more room for me."

We all struggle with selfishness. Children covet simple toys; adults crave adult toys.

What is the spiritual antidote for selfishness? How can we actively resist selfish impulses? The ministry of the One Anothers will provide powerful, consistent relief.

When I was growing up, I lived near a relative who, in retrospect, was one of the most selfish persons I have ever known. While writing this book, it occurred to me that he never engaged in any of the One Anothers. He never preferred others, never spoke encouraging words, was reluctant to greet others, never offered words of comfort, and never lifted a hand to help others. His selfishness prevented him from giving to others and kept him tethered to his own egocentric world. He lived a sad life.

All of the One Anothers require that we focus on others. Administering them is not about us; it's all about others. Instead of concentrating on our own needs, we'll be focusing on the needs of others. Instead of seeing the world through our own myopic perspective, we'll learn to view life from other people's perspectives. Because the One Anothers are to be ministered constantly, day after day, they will be a constant and consistent deterrent to our selfish tendencies.

A woman lived in a big-city neighborhood that was going downhill very fast. The area was becoming increasingly overcrowded, noisy, and dirty. It was a bad situation. The woman decided something would have to be done about it. She knew that she could change the situation if she had enough money. Consequently, she started a fund-raising drive. She called people. She sent letters. She got financial support from a private foundation. She finally raised eighty-five thousand dollars— and then used that money to move to another neighborhood.[2]

When we were in great need, God generously provided. He has given to us so that we can share with others. God doesn't intend for us to hoard his resources and "move to another neighborhood." He has given to us so that we can give to others.

The One Anothers are the antidote for selfishness.

Group Time—Session Two

Each member of the group should give his or her individual response to the first three questions. Allow about two minutes for each person's response. Allow all group members to share their answer to question #1 before proceeding to question #2.

1. What was the most interesting concept in this chapter?

2. Share about a time this week when you were able to prefer someone else and a time when you should have preferred someone else but did not.

3. Share your responses to the first three Personal Journal entries (page 25).

    As a group, process these discussion questions: [These discussion questions have been prioritized. Depending on the time allotted for your group discussion, you may not be able to process all the questions.]

    a. Ephesians 4:3 says, "Make every effort to keep the unity of the Spirit through the bond of peace." How will preferring one another help maintain peace and unity?

    b. How does someone who is in a position of authority balance the need to lead with the admonition to prefer others?

    c. As children we played the game of musical chairs. While it may have been fun to play, it was teaching the opposite of preferring others. How do we often play a subtle version of "musical chairs" in our day-to-day living?

    d. What can you do if you're in a relationship in which you always prefer another person, but he or she never prefers you?

    e. In recent years, the style of music used in worship has become a major issue in most churches; it is often a divisive issue. How could "Prefer One Another" be part of the solution for this challenge?

    f. How should we respond to someone who prefers us?

    g. On a scale from 1 to10 (1 being, "We're not too good at this" and 10 being, "We're really good at this"), how good is your church/organization at preferring other people?

    h. How will preferring other people be a testimony to "all men" (John 13:34) that we belong to the Lord and that we are his disciples?

    i. Read Romans 15:1. What does this verse teach us about preferring others?

    j. Read 1 Corinthians 7:32-34. What do these verses teach us about how husbands and wives should relate to each other?

    k. What can be done when two people prefer one another to the extent that it's hard to make a decision? (Bob: "I know you like Italian food, so let's go to Il Sorrento for dinner." Susan: "Thanks, honey, but I know you like barbecue. Let's go to Sonny Bryans.")

    l. How would you define a manipulative person? Why is this contrary to preferring others?

Homework:
Read and process chapter 3.

ACCEPT ONE ANOTHER

"Accept one another, then, just as Christ has accepted you" (Romans 15:7).

D r. Hudson Armerding, the former president of Wheaton College, sometime ago faced the dilemma of a particular problem brought on by prejudice. He stood before the students who had packed the chapel and made an announcement that got everyone's attention.

Because of the ramifications of prejudice, the school was facing the possibility of a financial crunch. A number of those who were heavy financial contributors to the college had been visiting the campus, and the word had spread that a number of the young men on campus were wearing their hair awfully long. And, in fact, a number of these Christian young men were now wearing beards. This had posed such a tremendous problem in the minds of those who supported the school financially that they were threatening to withdraw their support as some had already done. The student body sat quietly, anxiously awaiting the response of the administration.

Dr. Armerding began to scan the student body with his eyes. He finally spotted one young man, whom he called by name, and asked him to stand to his feet. He did, reluctantly. And then the president said, "I want you to come and join me on the platform." He did, with greater reluctance. He stood there with long hair and a long beard. Dr. Armerding, looking him straight in the face, said, "Young man, you have long hair and a long beard. You represent the very thing that these supporters of the school are against. I want you to know that the administration of this school does not feel as they do. We accept you and we love you. We believe you are here to seek and to find the truth as it is in the LORD Jesus Christ."

With that, the president reached out his arms, drew the young man to himself, and publicly embraced him, at which time the entire student body stood to its feet, giving spontaneous acclaim to this brave president.[1]

In this one, bold, courageous act, Dr. Armerding demonstrated to the student body one of the most powerful principles in Scripture—Accept One Another.

Gladys M. Hunt gives a telling description of acceptance when she writes:

> Acceptance means you are valuable just as you are. It allows you to be the real you. You are not forced into someone else's idea of who you are. It means your ideas are taken seriously since they reflect you. You can talk about how you feel inside, why you feel that way, and someone really cares. Acceptance means you can try out your ideas without being shot down. You can even express heretical thoughts and discuss them with intelligent questioning. You feel safe. No one will pronounce judgment on you even though they don't agree with you. It doesn't mean you'll never be corrected or shown to be wrong. It simply means it's safe to be you and no one will destroy you out of prejudice.[2]

The ministry of Jesus was predicated upon accepting people. He erased the artificial boundaries of culture and status, looked beyond people's sin, and accepted people. He touched lepers, ate with sinners, visited the homes of tax collectors, and washed the feet of the betrayer. Through these countless loving acts, Jesus made a clear statement: "Never will I withhold my love from you; there will never be a time or circumstance when I will refuse to love you." It was as though barriers didn't exist.

For instance, it must have shocked the disciples to see Jesus talking to a woman he met at Jacob's well (John 4:1–42). Not only was she a woman, but she was also a Samaritan; and in Jewish culture it was not proper for men to speak publicly to either. Furthermore, she was a woman of ill repute. Yet Jesus conversed with her. This most likely caused a stir among the disciples; indeed the Bible says they "were surprised to find him talking with a woman" (v. 27). But they observed him *accepting* this woman and no doubt noticed the profound impact it had on her life: "Many of the Samaritans from that town believed in him because of the woman's testimony" (v. 39).

Indeed, the Bible says that Jesus' willingness to accept us was an integral part of our first coming to know him: "While we were yet sinners, Christ died for us" (Romans 5:8). God didn't say, "Shape up, and then I'll send my Son to help." If God accepts us unconditionally, shouldn't we accept others in like manner?

The apostle Paul told the church at Rome to "accept one another as God has accepted you" because he himself had been touched deeply by God's acceptance of him. As part of his personal testimony, he wrote, "Christ Jesus came into the world to save sinners—of whom I am the worst. But for that very reason I was shown mercy so that in me, the worst of sinners, Christ Jesus might display his unlimited patience as an example for those who would believe on him and receive eternal life" (1Timothy 1:15–16).

> Acceptance means you can try out your ideas without being shot down. It doesn't mean you'll never be corrected or shown to be wrong. It simply means it's safe to be you and no one will destroy you out of prejudice.

One of the fundamental needs of human beings is to be accepted.

Through the years, we all develop our own personal theory of human psychology; we all have a personal perspective on how humans "work"—how we're "wired." Our understanding is shaped by our family heritage, our religious background, our understanding of the Bible, and what we've learned at school, on the playground, and in the office, among many other factors. We inevitably develop a lens through which we view human beings (including ourselves). Though we may have never officially articulated our beliefs, they inevitably affect how we view and treat others and ourselves.

Relative to how humans "work," we need to embrace these two fundamental facts:

1. Every human is *the same* in that, having been created in the image of God, we all have intrinsic worth and value.
2. Every human is *unique* in that God created each of us as "one of a kind."

Upon these two theological/philosophical pillars rests the grace gift of acceptance. They also provide some practical insights into how we are to accept others.

Statements of Acceptance

1. **I will willingly receive you and love you because you are a human being.**

   We are to accept people because of their intrinsic value; there is immense value in *who* a person is, separate and apart from what they *do*. It is the difference between valuing a human *being* versus a human *doing*. We accept people based on the following facts:

   - Everyone is created in God's image (Genesis 1:27). Despite differences of opinion as to what this actually involves, the bottom line is this: There is something Godlike in every human, and whatever it is, it is of great value.

   - Jesus died for *all* men (2 Corinthians 5:15). Even though all people do not *receive* God's gift of eternal life, nevertheless, God has paid the price for all men. We have value because we have been purchased at a high price (1 Peter 1:18–19).

   - Every human is of inestimable value. In Matthew 16:26, Jesus asks, "What good will it be for a man if he gains the whole world, yet forfeits his soul?" In this one verse, Jesus established the fact that one human soul is more valuable than all that is in the world. The combined wealth, knowledge, and resources of the globe are not more valuable than one person.

   [handwritten: HE HAD IT ALL BUT STILL NOT ENOUGH TO ___ HIS SOUL!]

2. **I will acknowledge, affirm, and delight in the fact that you are unique.** *[handwritten: — GOD LIKES VARIETY]*

   God created every person *unique*. Scientists tell us that no two snowflakes are identical. If God takes the effort to make snowflakes unique, rest assured, God doesn't clone humans. In accepting others, we are essentially agreeing with God that he has created all things well; we are affirming our belief that God's creation is "good." To the contrary, if we refuse to accept others, we are essentially challenging the Creator and his handiwork by saying, "God, you must have blown it on this one."

   Jesus taught this truth when he said, "He who receives me receives the one who sent me" (Matthew 10:40) and, "He who rejects me rejects him who sent me" (Luke 10:16).

   Write down the names of two family members and the ways in which they are unique.

   Family member _____

   Unique characteristics _____

   [handwritten: ALSO I HAVE DIFF ACCEPT'S THIS PERSN — LIST AN AREA I HAVE TRB TO]
   [handwritten: HOW CAN I BE MORE ACCEPT TO THIS PERSON ___ WITH THEM ___]

   Family member _____

   Unique characteristics _____

3. **I will willingly receive you and love you, even though you are different from me.**

We're particularly challenged to accept people who look, talk, dress, or behave differently, have different customs, are of a different nationality, or hold to different beliefs. We normally don't struggle with accepting those who are like us.

Most of us have a rather limited view of life. For instance, I was born in America, raised in the south, reared in a Christian family, attended a conservative church, and for thirty years have ministered in a similar environment. While I don't begrudge my heritage, I must realize that it has created a telescopic lens through which I view the world and it has shaped my view of life. My challenge is to accept each of the six billion people on the face of the earth even though they aren't cut from the same fabric.

A church I served at several years ago was challenged in this area of acceptance when a homosexual man began attending the services. After attending for several months, he wrote the ministerial staff a compelling letter. Part of the letter read:

I've been attending your church for several months now and have felt genuine love from so many people. However, several weeks ago something happened that was quite hurtful. Following a morning service I was walking out to the parking lot to go home. When I got to my car, one of your church members had ripped off a Gay Rights bumper sticker from my car. When he realized the car belonged to me, he stuck the bumper sticker in my face and said, "This stuff isn't wanted around here."

Fortunately, this one incident did not deter the man from coming back to church. As a matter of fact, the story has a happy ending. The church body, as a whole, continued to befriend and accept him, and this general acceptance of the body of Christ attracted him to God and led him to accept Christ as his Savior. Perhaps it was because Jesus (and Jesus' body, the church) *accepted* him as he was that he *accepted* Jesus as he is.

Perhaps

it was because Jesus *accepted* him as he was
that he *accepted* Jesus as he is.

Refer back to what you wrote at the end of statement #2 (regarding the unique characteristics of two of your family members). In what ways do you have difficulty in accepting them because of their uniqueness?

_____

_____

4. **I will be particularly sensitive to accept you when you enter a new environment.**

We should be particularly sensitive to people's need for acceptance when they enter into a new environment such as a new school, church, or workplace. When thrust into a new environment, the first emotional issue a person faces is, "Will I be accepted?"

[Handwritten margin notes:]
- race
- status
- culture
- status < money
          manners
- lifestyle
   - poor/rich
   - type of work
   - spending
   - sexual
- religion

we must be very careful to separate god's word from a person from what they do, say, act, say.

Write down the names of several people who have just entered into your environment, which for them is a new environment. (For instance, someone who just joined your church or someone who recently went to work in your office.) How could you pro-actively accept them?

Name _____

How I could express acceptance to this person:

_____

Name _____

How I could express acceptance to this person:

_____

5. **I will not neglect ministering any and all of the One Anothers to you.**

I WILL NOT SHOW FAVORITISM

A reluctance to accept people will cause us to discriminate against some and to favor others. This prejudice may even cause us to withhold giving the One Anothers to some while giving them freely to others.

But when we freely accept all people, favoritism gives way to unconditional love: This attitude says, "I will be kind to you, despite your behavior. I will greet you even though you haven't bathed. I will not refuse to affirm your worth, even though I disapprove of your lifestyle." In essence, "I will forgive, encourage, comfort, prefer [insert all thirty-five of the One Anothers] you, regardless of who you are, what you have done, or what you will do." This is the same consistency of love that we enjoy from God (Romans 8:38–39).

This attitude is foundational to consistently obeying the 11th Commandment. Without it, we become pickers and choosers, deciding who is worthy of receiving love and who isn't. Acceptance means that because each human is created in the image of God, we are *all* worthy of receiving *all* the One Anothers.

6. **Even as I get to know you on a deep level, I will not stop accepting you.**

AS I GET TO KNOW YOU, I WILL NOT REJECT YOU - EVEN IF I DISCOVER SOMETHING I DON'T LIKE OR AGREE WITH.

While we are often challenged to accept people whom we do not know well (or perhaps those whom we have just encountered), we are also continually challenged to accept people whom we *do* know well (our family and friends). For instance, we may be reluctant to accept a young person who just walked into our church because his hair is dyed purple ("Our kids don't look like that."), but we may be just as reluctant to accept our spouse who just walked into church ten minutes late ("She's always late. We've talked about this so many times. Her tardiness is a constant source of irritation to me so I'll just ignore her for a while.") Oftentimes it's actually more difficult to accept someone we know well because the closer we are to a person, the more clearly we see his flaws, inconsistencies, weaknesses, and yes, his sin. These irritants are exacerbated because we spend so much time with those with whom we are close.

Of course, we will be more prompted to accept others just as *they are* if we will remember our own need to be accepted just the way *we are*. For instance, my wife is always late. I've nicknamed her "the late Mary McMinn." Quite frankly, it's been a struggle dealing with this, because my handle is "Mr. Punctual." But I'm more willing to accept Mary's lateness when I realize that I'm also know as "Mr. Impatience." For most of my married life, I've struggled with being curt and abrasive with Mary. When I recognize my own personal weakness, and my need for acceptance despite it, I am more inclined to accept Mary in spite of her tardiness.

I WILL STRIVE TO GET TO KNOW YOU AND WILL NOT REJECT YOU
o EVEN IF I'M INITIALLY CHALLENGED
o EVEN IF IN THE PROCESS, I DISCOVER SOMETHING I DO NOT LIKE/AGREE WITH

One night we had several couples over to our house for dinner. After we ate, we sat in the den and began to share about our lives. The sharing quickly reached a deep, vulnerable level.

One couple, who had recently joined our church, hesitantly shared that, in the early years of their marriage, they had gone through some rough times in their relationship. They had even divorced and then remarried each other. I was touched and blessed by their sharing. I remember thinking, *What a wonderful testimony to the redeeming work of Christ.*

> Acceptance means that because each human is created in the image of God, we are all worthy of receiving all the One Anothers.

Later, they told me that when they got in their car to go home, they began to regret their vulnerable sharing. Ten years earlier, when they were at a different church, they had shared their story to some church members who took the information, used it against them, and piously rejected them because of their divorce. The betrayal hurt so deeply that they stayed out of church for years.

Because of their vulnerable sharing in our home, they just assumed that it would happen again.

The next Sunday, when I saw them at church, the Lord reminded me that after people vulnerably share they are particularly needful of acceptance and approval. So I went up to them, hugged them warmly, and said, "I want you two to know that I appreciated your vulnerability at our home the other night and that I love you dearly and will always love you. It doesn't matter what you've done in the past. It doesn't matter what you may do in the future. I love you and accept you."

Unbeknownst to me, that 60 second conversation made a huge impact on them. They knew that they had been accepted, despite their past struggles and disappointments. Later, they told me, "From that moment on, Don, we became your biggest fans and supporters." Indeed, for years now, they have been a tremendous blessing to my family, my ministry, and me.

7. **I'm going to accept you for who you are; I won't always be trying to change you.**

Many family relationships are under constant strain because we feel "called of God" to be his change agents in the lives of others.

- "I'm called to be heavenly sandpaper in your life."
- "Your mother didn't do a very good job raising you—I'm taking over."
- "My main job as your parent is to perfect your character and personality."

The truth is, our greatest calling is to love and accept our family members—just as they are—and to trust God to bring about any changes he deems necessary. It's not that we shouldn't be interested in or involved in the character development of our loved ones; that just shouldn't be our first priority. Nitpicking at someone's weaknesses and faults will constantly strain the relationship and may even create an adversarial role one toward another.

Sure, there are areas of every person's life that need work:

- "You're so absent-minded."
- "Why do you start talking halfway through a thought? It doesn't make any sense."
- "You're so slow in the mornings."
- "Why can't you remember to record the checks that you write?"
- "Why don't you talk more when we're around other people?"
- "You talk too much when we're around other people."

But the question is, Are we willing to totally love and accept people despite their weaknesses, idiosyncrasies, and faults? Furthermore, will our deep and abiding love prompt us to "cover over" these areas? First Peter 4:8 presents a powerful challenge: "Above all, love each other deeply, because love covers over a multitude of sins." I don't know about you, but I struggle with "covering over" simple, minor irritations that I have in my relationships with my wife and daughters, much less their sins.

- If your spouse is overweight, are you willing to patiently love her and be sensitive to protect her in public?
- If your spouse is usually tardy, are you quick to point out his fault and embarrass him in public?
- If your child struggles with shyness, will you try to protect her?

It's amazing how our accepting others often provides the motivation and grace for them to change. Those irritating areas in other people's lives—that we have unsuccessfully tried to change through confrontation and manipulation—often begin to miraculously change when we accept them just the way they are. For instance, when I finally learned to accept Mary despite her tendency to be tardy, she actually became more punctual.

As we increasingly embrace the ministry of acceptance, we'll become more open, friendly, and consistent with people. Also, we'll be less susceptible to these relational diseases: prejudice, narrow-mindedness, bigotry, intolerance, discrimination, chauvinism, injustice, and favoritism.

What are some unique aspects of your spouse (or if you're single, a friend) that you have tried to change? _____

_____

Practical Ways to Accept One Another

1. **Be particularly sensitive to demonstrate acceptance to someone who has just shared vulnerably with you.**

   For instance, after someone shares with you a personal weakness, besetting sin, or a shameful experience from his past, he needs to be reassured that what he shared with you will not disrupt your relationship and that you still accept him even though you now know some of the painful aspects of his life.

2. **Be particularly sensitive to demonstrate acceptance to people who may suffer a poor self-image or whose self confidence has been challenged.**
   A person's need for acceptance is accentuated when he feels like he has failed (real or perceived), when he is disappointed in himself, or when he is insecure about who he is and his self-worth.
   Go out of your way to accept someone when:
   - He's fired from his job.
   - She strikes out at the bottom of the ninth inning with the bases loaded.
   - She loses the big sale.
   - He feels inadequate for his job.
   - She feels unlovely.
   - He can't seem to get "on track" in life.

3. **When you're meeting someone for the first time:**

- Take the initiative to greet him.
- After the initial greeting, continue to talk to him; the process of greeting will soon evolve into accepting. In other words, a short greeting does not necessarily convey acceptance.
- Make a concerted effort to make him feel comfortable ("Why don't you sit next to me?"); and if possible, include him in activities ("Let me get you a folder and a nametag so you can join the group.")
- If possible, introduce him to others in the group.
- Following the initial contact, make a follow-up call or visit. This will reinforce the fact that you do indeed accept him; the first encounter wasn't just a fluke or an insincere act.

4. **When you're challenged to accept someone you already know well:**

- Realize that there are areas of your life that others find hard to accept.
- Realize that the closer we get to a person, the more we notice his flaws, weaknesses, and other areas that irritate us. This is a natural part of developing close relationships. But this also means that often, the closer we get to someone the more difficult it is to accept him.
- Realize that we are to accept others as God has accepted us (Romans 15:7) and that he has accepted us "just as we are"; therefore we are to accept others "just as they are."
- Realize that there is immense value in *who a person is*, separate and apart from *what they do* (sometimes they may "do right" and sometimes they may "do wrong"). Acceptance is based on who a person is, not what they do.
- Francis Schaeffer once made a suggestion as to how we can "love our enemies" (Luke 6:27). He suggested that when we are faced with the task of loving our enemies, we should close our eyes, picture our best friend, meditate on how we would interact with this friend, then open our eyes and interact with our enemy in like manner.
- Imagine the person you're having difficulty accepting, saying to you, "Would you please love me without trying to change me?"

A Lesson from Billy

In the early years of my ministry, there was a young man in our church named Billy. In many ways Billy was a challenge to accept. He thought a bath every two or three days was sufficient, and I often wondered whether he even owned a toothbrush. Billy was extremely faithful to come to church, and he felt obliged to come up to me after every service and engage in lengthy conversation. He was like a heat-seeking missile—once he locked on to you, he was hard to shake loose. He wanted to tell me how his week had gone, his plans for the next week, ad nauseam.

In time, I became so bothered by Billy that I began to actively avoid him. When I saw him coming, I would walk the other way or begin talking to someone else with my back to Billy. When conversation with him was unavoidable, I would cut it off after only a few sentences. I had lost all patience with him.

One day, during a prayer time, my conscience began to bother me regarding my attitude toward Billy. I argued with God, telling him how repulsive Billy could be at times and finished my argument with the fact that it was unfair and unreasonable for Billy to expect me to spend so much time with him when there were others who also needed my attention.

God silenced my grumbling with one sentence: "Don, you're my Billy."

God silenced my grumbling with one sentence: "Don, you're my Billy."

He then went on to explain: "Don, you often come to me having only taken a spiritual bath every two or three days, and you're usually selfish in what you want to talk about—you only want to talk about what you're doing. But Don, I never reject you. When I see you coming, I don't turn my back and ignore you. I always accept you, just the way you are. I want you to accept Billy, just the way he is."

Yes, we are to see in other people what Jesus saw in us and we are to receive others as he receives us.

Pause for a moment and consider your own need for acceptance. You'll probably feel the pain of those times you were not accepted.

Mom's Investment

 ■ Regarding people, Mom was color-blind, class-blind, and status-blind. She treated all people the same. She did seem to have a penchant for the down-and-out—for years she taught a Sunday school class for kids who came to church on buses—but she accepted everyone. I don't ever remember hearing my mother utter a prejudicial statement. ■ And Mom accepted me. In many ways I was very different from Mom. She was quite reserved and always wanted to play it safe. My life was a bit more edgy: I was parachuting in high school, drove from Dallas to Acapulco one Christmas Eve, purchased my first house when I was a junior in college, finished my Ph.D. when I was twenty-seven years old, etc. But Mom never tried to hold me back or change me. Although I'm sure my lifestyle at times frightened her, she never rode the brakes. She let me be who I was. ■ Not only did she accept and affirm my uniqueness, she helped establish my sense of self-worth. Mom made me feel like I was somebody special, not because of what I did, but simply because I was a human being (and her wonderful son). ■ Perhaps the greatest gift a parent can give a child is to accept him just as he is. ■ Thanks, Mom.

Write your own definition of Accept One Another.

_____

_____

_____

Personal Journal

1. Write about a time in your life when someone accepted you and it deeply impacted your life.

_____

_____

Write about a time in your life when you were hurt because someone did not accept you.

_____

2. Write about the last time you were challenged to accept someone, and you did. Write about the last time you were challenged to accept someone, but you didn't. _____

_____

_____

3. Write about a time when you observed someone else accepting others. _____

_____

_____

4. What type of person are you most likely not to accept? Search your heart for any areas in which you may hold a prejudice against a particular group of people. For instance: "I don't like teenagers with long hair." "I try to avoid people who talk too much." "I prefer not to be around a particular race." "People who are lazy really bother me." "I think people from the Northeast are rude; I wish they would stay put." In other words, what is it about some people that really irritates you?

I often struggle accepting _____

_____

5. Consider those people you are closest to—your immediate family and friends. What are some characteristics about each person that, at times, make it difficult to totally accept them? ("My husband is sloppy." "My daughter sleeps too much." "My wife is always late." "My father is so narrow-minded." "My aunt is so ultra-conservative.")

Name	Characteristic
_____	_____
_____	_____
_____	_____
_____	_____

6. What are some of *your* unique characteristics or flaws that other people may find hard to accept?

_____

_____

7. A prerequisite for accepting others is accepting yourself. We will be reluctant to accept a friend—despite his faults—if we do not first realize that we are of great value to God. Have you accepted yourself? In what areas do you have a hard time accepting yourself?

_____

_____

8. What can you do this week to accept your two secret recipients?

Secret recipient _____

Unchurched secret recipient _____

9. On a scale from 1 to 10 (1 being, "I need to greatly improve" and 10 being, "I do a good job"), how well do you accept others? Ask your OA Partner to rate you.

I rated myself a _____.

My OA partner rated me a _____.

Practical Suggestion #2

As we minister the One Anothers, we should prioritize our closest relationships (spouse, parents, children, family, and friends).

Several years ago, the Lord "customized" Acts 1:4, 8 to my life. The verses read, "Do not leave Jerusalem, but wait for the gift my Father promised, which you have heard me speak about ... but you will receive power when the Holy Spirit comes on you; and you will be my witnesses in Jerusalem, and in all Judea and Samaria, and to the ends of the earth." These words, spoken by Jesus, gave the disciples a strategy and a sense of priority for sharing the gospel with others. In essence, he said, "Wait until you get the Spirit yourself and then share it with those closest to you (Jerusalem). Then, once the gospel permeates that area, go to the next larger section (Judea), then to the next (Samaria), and finally to the ends of the earth." I visualize a set of concentric circles; Jesus was telling his disciples to start in the center and work their way to the outside.

> It's been said that who we are at home is who we really are.

I realize that in these verses Jesus was referring to geographical areas, but when he spoke to my heart about these verses, I saw the various concentric circles through the lens of relationships. For me, "Jerusalem" is my wife, Mary; "Judea" is my two daughters, Sarah and Lauren; "Samaria" is my set of close friends; and "the ends of the earth" is everyone else. In short, the Lord challenged me with this idea: "Let's see if you can live the gospel—everything you believe and teach about the Christian life—with just one person, your wife. If you can't live the gospel with her, don't try to share it with others. Then see if you can live the gospel with just two other people, your daughters. Once you're on the right track at home, try it out with some close friends. Only after you've learned to make it work in these relationships should you share it with the world."

Makes sense, doesn't it? The family structure, among other things, is a laboratory in which we can experiment, fail, learn, and succeed at "Love One Another." These are the people we're around every day. They know who we really are; they not only see our Sunday smile, but also our Monday frown. It's been said that who we are at home is who we really are.

But often we start with the outer circle and try to work our way back to the center. We minister to all the needy, hurting people in the world but neglect our own families. This wrong priority is not only hypocritical, but it also significantly reduces our effectiveness and authority in ministry.

The apostle Paul spoke often of this issue:

- "Put [your] religion into practice by caring for [your] own family" (1 Timothy 5:4).
- "If anyone does not provide for his relatives, and especially for his immediate family, he has denied the faith and is worse than an unbeliever" (1 Timothy 5:8).
- "Do good to all people, especially to those who belong to the family of believers" (Galatians 6:10).

Relative to the 11th Commandment, the implication is obvious—we must begin with our closest family members.

For instance, when learning to "Greet One Another," we should prioritize our family. While writing the chapter on Greet One Another, I realized that quite often when I arrive home after work, I immediately check the mail, make myself a cup of coffee, and change clothes before I take the initiative to greet Mary and ask about her day.

The same sense of priority should apply to Comfort One Another. One day, when I was at home, I received a call from a lady in our church whose cat had died. She was quite upset, and I comforted her over the phone. Mary overheard the conversation and was saddened and hurt by the fact that I was willing to spend twenty minutes comforting a church member over the phone—about a cat—but I was often reluctant to comfort her when she needed it. With Mary, my response was often, "Just get over it; you'll be fine."

As you work through this book and begin to minister the One Anothers, start with your family first.

List the names of your immediate family members and your closest friends.

_____

_____

_____

_____

_____

Is it hard for you to minister the One Anothers to your closest family members? Why?

_____

_____

_____

Powerful Result #2

The more we "do" the One Anothers, we become more like Christ.

In Chapter 1, we learned that although the One Anothers are initially acts that we *do*, eventually they become part of who we *are*; they help forge our character. For instance, as I continually comfort others, I will become an empathizing person. As I continually greet people, I will become a friendly person. The goal is that eventually my actions will become a natural outflow of who I am.

This process of inward change is called *sanctification*—a fancy theological word that simply means that during our earthly journey we are progressively being conformed to the image of Christ—his inward image. Ephesians 5:1 urges us to "be imitators of God." Romans 8:29 says that we are to be "conformed to the likeness of Jesus."

The sixty-four-million-dollar question is: How do we do that? How do we sign up for the course on sanctification? While there are, no doubt, multiple ways to be conformed to the image of Christ (reading the Bible, prayer, meditation, etc.), an effective strategy is simply to incorporate the One Anothers into our daily lifestyle.

The One Anothers are a practical guide to how we can have the same mind and heart attitude of Christ. When he met the Samaritan woman—he accepted her; at the tomb of Lazarus—he comforted Mary and Martha; on the night he was betrayed—he served his disciples; after his resurrection—he affirmed Peter; and when he "said not a word"—he preferred us.

Jesus' physical appearance is never described in the Bible, and for good reason. If we knew what he looked like, we would idolize those physical traits. But we do know what he "looked like" on the inside. He was kind, compassionate, patient … all the desirable character traits you can list. It is these inward traits that we should strive to emulate, and the One Anothers provide for us a practical curriculum for training.

List several characteristics of Jesus that you would like to emulate. Which of the One Anothers would help you develop these traits?

Aspect of Jesus' character	Corresponding One Another
_____	_____
_____	_____
_____	_____

Group Time—Session Three

Each member of the group should give his or her individual response to the first four questions. Allow about two minutes for each person's response. Allow all group members to share their answer to question #1 before proceeding to question #2.

1. What was the most interesting concept in this chapter?

2. Referring back to last week's lesson, share about a time this week when you were able to prefer someone else and a time when you should have preferred someone else but did not.

3. Share your responses to the first three Personal Journal entries in this chapter (page 40).

4. Which areas of self-doubt have you often struggled with? (For instance: physical appearance, lack of education, lack of social skills, embarrassment regarding family of origin, past failures, etc.)

    As each person vulnerably shares, speak words of acceptance to him: "God loves you, and I love you, regardless of _____ [the details of what he just shared]. And I accept you just the way you are. You're a person of great worth. You're important to me and this group."

    As a group, process these discussion questions: [These discussion questions have been prioritized. Depending on the time allotted for your group discussion, you may not be able to process all the questions.]

a.   Romans 15:7 instructs us to accept others as God has accepted us. As a group, discuss this question: How did God accept us? (See Romans 5:8; Acts 10:28; Acts 10:34–35.)

b.   What do cliques have to do with accepting or not accepting people? Why does a clique feel so comfortable? How do cliques impact our willingness to accept others?

c.   Opportunities to travel (particularly internationally) will often help us become more accepting of others. Why is this?

d.   It's been said that "justice is blind." What does that mean? Should acceptance be "blind"?

e.   Why should we accept someone even if we don't agree with his theological, political, or philosophical position?

f.   On a scale from 1 to 10 (1 being, "We're not too good at this" and 10 being, "We're really good at this"), how good is your church/organization at accepting people?

g.   Reread Romans 15:7 and notice the last phrase. How does our accepting others "bring praise to God?"

h.   What type of environment is created when we as individuals and/or our organization (church, small group, school) become(s) an accepting person/place?

i.   How will accepting other people be a testimony to "all men" (John 13:34) that we belong to the Lord and that we are his disciples?

j.   Read Acts 10:9–28, the account of Peter's vision regarding eating clean and unclean meat. What lesson did Peter learn, and what can we learn, about accepting others.

Homework:

Read and process chapter 4.

GREET ONE ANOTHER
"Greet one another with a holy kiss" (Romans 16:16).

Peggy Noonan, speechwriter for Ronald Reagan, relates a story about Frances Green, an eighty-three-year old woman who lived by herself on Social Security in a town just outside San Francisco. She had little money, but for eight years she'd been sending one dollar a year to the Republican National Convention.

Then one day Frances got a RNC fund-raising letter in the mail, a beautiful piece on thick, cream-colored paper with black-and-gold lettering. It invited the recipient to come to the White House to meet President Ronald Reagan. She never noticed the little RSVP card that suggested a positive reply needed to be accompanied by a generous donation. She thought she'd been invited because they appreciated her dollar-a-year support.

Frances scraped up every cent she had and took a four-day train ride across America. Unable to afford a sleeper, she slept sitting up in coach. Finally she arrived at the White House gate: a little elderly woman with white hair, white powder all over her face, white stockings, an old hat with white netting, and an all-white dress, now yellow with age. When she got up to the guard at the gate and gave her name, however, the man frowned, glanced over his official list, and told her that her name wasn't there. She couldn't go in. Frances Green was heartbroken.

A Ford Motor Company executive who was standing in line behind her watched and listened to the little scenario. Realizing something was wrong, he pulled Frances aside and got her story. Then he asked her to return at nine o'clock the next morning and meet him there. She agreed. In the meantime, he made contact with Anne

Higgins, a presidential aide, and got a clearance to give her a tour of the White House and introduce her to the president. Reagan agreed to see her, "of course."

The next day was anything but calm and easy at the White House. Ed Meese had just resigned. There had been a military uprising abroad. Reagan was in and out of high-level secret sessions. But Frances Green showed up at nine o'clock, full of expectation and enthusiasm.

The executive met her, gave her a wonderful tour of the White House, then quietly led her by the Oval Office, thinking maybe, at best, she might get a quick glimpse of the president on her way out. Members of the National Security Council came out. High-ranking generals were coming and going. In the midst of all the hubbub, President Reagan glanced out and saw Frances Green. With a smile, he gestured her into his office.

As she entered, he rose from his desk and called out, "Frances! Those computers fouled up again! If I'd have known you were coming I would have come out there to get you myself." He then invited her to sit down, and they talked leisurely about California, her town, her life, and her family.

The President of the United States gave Frances Green a lot of time that day—more time than he had. Some would say it was time wasted. But those who say that didn't know Ronald Reagan. He knew this woman had nothing to give him, but she needed something he could give her. And so he (as well as the Ford executive) took time to be kind and compassionate.[1]

President Reagan greeted Frances, and it deeply impacted her life, his life, and the lives of those around them.

Numerous times in Scripture we see the simple but powerful ministry of Greeting One Another. Because it is so simple to perform and takes only a few seconds, we often underestimate the importance of this ministry and mistakenly assume that we all know *how* to greet others.

So let's learn the why and how of greeting others.

Why Is It Important to Greet One Another?

1. **Greeting is the prelude to ministering the other One Anothers.**

    As discussed in chapter 2, three of the One Anothers must precede the remaining thirty-one, and they best come in this order: Prefer One Another, Accept One Another, and Greet One Another. So greeting others is one of the "preludes" to the other One Anothers. Often, it is the first step, the initial action. When coming in contact with someone, we may not know immediately what this person's current need is, that is, which of the One Anothers is needed. Does this person need comfort? Support? Encouragement? It often takes a few minutes of conversation to determine the need, but it is always appropriate to greet someone. A warm, sincere greeting is the first step. It only takes thirty to ninety seconds to greet someone, and then we can transition into one of the other One Anothers.

    In chapter 2, we discovered that to Prefer One Another is the *initial attitude* that motivates us to engage in the other One Anothers; unless we are willing to prefer others, we'll be reticent to greet, encourage, support, comfort and forgive them.

    In chapter 3, we discussed the next step—Accept One Another. So while preferring and accepting others are often the initial *attitudes*—to greet others is often the first *action*.

2. **A warm greeting communicates several important messages:**

    - "If I haven't met you, I want to know you."
    - "If I already know you, I want to know how you're doing."
    - "I want to acknowledge your presence because you are welcome here."
    - "I want to affirm your inestimable value as a person."

3. **Greeting communicates to others the condition of the relationship.**

    Greeting communicates that, even if the relationship is strained, we want to maintain contact so the relationship can be healed. Luke 15 tells the beautiful story of the prodigal son. Verse 20 records the father's response to the news that his son is coming home: "But while he was still a long way off, his father saw him and was filled with compassion for him; he ran to his son, threw his arms around him and kissed him." Notice the father's initiative; feel the effect of his passionate greeting.

    Greeting someone is always apropos and valuable, but when a relationship is strained, an aggressive, warm greeting is critical and powerfully effective.

    I remember a time when I had a slight misunderstanding with my boss. It meant a lot to me when he came down to my office, greeted me, and said that he wanted to talk about the tension we felt.

    Greeting someone regularly also provides a continuous opportunity to keep the relationship "current" and helps preserve the health of a relationship. Particularly in close relationships, it is important to maintain constant communication so that both parties are reassured of the health of the relationship. For example, if I walk past my assistant's desk and enter my office without greeting her, she may wonder, *Is Don upset? Have I done something to upset him?* If I'm at church and walk past a friend in the hall without greeting him, he may think, *Is Don mad at me for not returning his phone call?* Such ambiguity is fodder for unhealthy "self-talk" and it gives the enemy an opportunity to lie to us about the condition of our relationships.

    > Greeting someone is always apropos and valuable, but when a relationship is strained, an aggressive, warm greeting is critical and powerfully effective.

    Years ago I worked for an organization that was headquartered in another city. I worked out of my house. Sometimes I would go several weeks without talking to my boss. The longer we went without any conversation, the more insecure I would become. My self-talk would cause me to wonder, *Is everything okay? Have I forgotten to do something?* I don't think I suffered from extreme paranoia; I just needed regular contact to affirm the condition of the relationship.

    If we will regularly greet those whom we are close to, it will let them know the condition of the relationship.

    Describe a time in your life when one of your relationships was strained and a greeting would have helped clarify the situation.

    _____

    _____

4. **If we don't greet other people, we may appear unfriendly, aloof, moody, apathetic, self-centered, and unconcerned.**

A church member once accused me of being unfriendly and aloof. The comment shocked me because I knew in my heart that I always wanted to be just the opposite. When I asked her what I had done to make her feel that way she said, "Sometimes at church, you'll pass me in the hall and not say anything to me." My perspective on this was, "Sundays are very busy for me. I have to negotiate a tight schedule that includes multiple services. I just don't have time to talk to everyone I might see in the hallways." But my perspective was wrong.

To come into the presence of another human being and not to acknowledge her presence is being unfriendly. I have since learned to offer a brief, two to five-second greeting to everyone I see. At least a "Hi, good to see you." I've also learned to allow more time to get from point A to point B so that I will have adequate time to greet people. I figure that it will take me about ninety seconds to walk from my office to the sanctuary, so I allow about four minutes so I can have time to greet people. I also build in some "Greet One Another" time after the last worship service. Instead of heading to the car immediately after the service is over, I designate about fifteen minutes to visit with people.

The truth is, if we neglect greeting others, we probably *are* unfriendly and self-centered. It's not just that we may *appear* to be unfriendly; we probably *are* unfriendly.

When you're at your office or at church, do you take time to greet people? Explain your answer.

_____

_____

5. **Greeting others affirms their value as a human being.**

Why should we greet others? What is the underlying reason for greeting? Is it a patronizing gesture? Is it just an obligation we must fulfill? Is it simply our duty, a necessary prelude to other, more important functions?

No.

We Greet One Another because every human being has inestimable value and is worthy of being acknowledged and affirmed. When we greet someone, we are saying, "You are important. You matter. You have great value."

As discussed earlier in this chapter, greeting people is often the first step in the process of ministering to them; it is the prelude to the other One Anothers. But this doesn't mean it is a trivial formality. A genuine greeting delivers a significant message—"You are important!"

6. **When we greet others we let them know that we are approachable.**

A side benefit of Greeting One Another is that we will become approachable; people will feel comfortable initiating conversation with us and being around us.

First, let's establish the fact that approachableness is a noble and admirable character quality. The opposite is to be aloof, detached, standoffish, unapproachable, and even arrogant and condescending. Don't be that way.

It's interesting to note that Jesus was so approachable that everyone—children, sinners, and the outcasts of society—sensed that he was accessible and easy to talk to, and they felt comfortable in his presence.

When I was in college, I had the privilege to meet, on two separate occasions, Billy Graham and Bill Bright, two of the greatest Christian leaders of our century. I only spent about two minutes with each man, but I distinctly remember noticing how gracious each man was during those two minutes. They each treated me as if I had every right in the world to talk to them. Our conversation was brief only because there were hundreds of other people who wanted to visit with them. There was absolutely no hint of, "I'm too good to be talking to a young kid."

We should never have an intimidating, daunting demeanor; that's not godly. And one of the best ways to guard against this vice is to continually Greet One Another, because in so doing, we convey the message that we are indeed approachable.

Practical Ways to Greet One Another

1. **Prioritize people over things.**

Realize that in any situation, the most important commodity is people. The most valuable thing that can happen in any situation is what can and should happen in the hearts of people.

- We should never be so focused on getting the meeting started that we neglect greeting everyone. Agendas are not more important than people.
- Getting the job done is not more important than the people involved in the job.
- When eating dinner with a group of people, the people are more important than the menu, the table setting, and the food.

This principle—prioritize people over things—should be a rule of thumb for all of the One Anothers, but it particularly applies to greeting people. Whatever time and energy it takes to properly and adequately greet people is worth the investment.

2. **Be proactive in greeting others; take the initiative.**

Don't wait for other people to greet you; take the initiative. Don't think, *I'll greet them if they'll greet me.* Be proactive. If you're at a dinner party, take the initiative to greet every person in the house. Approach people with the intent to welcome them.

3. **Greet people one at a time.**

At times, it may be appropriate to express greetings to a group of people. For instance, a guest speaker at a banquet may say to a large audience, "My wife and I bring you our greetings." But whenever possible, greet people individually. The phrase "one another" implies a one-to-one approach and this personal touch is particularly important when we Greet One Another. So when you enter a room and there are five people there, instead of saying, "Hi, gang"; take the time to greet each person individually.

4. **When in a group of people, if possible, greet everyone in the group; otherwise you may show favoritism.**

Philippians 4:21 teaches us to "greet *all* the saints" (emphasis added). (Also see Hebrews 13:24.) In Matthew 5:47, Jesus taught, "And if you greet only your brothers, what are you doing more than others? Do not even pagans do that?"

One of the basic "rules" of the One Anothers is that we should minister them to *all people.* Let's apply this principle to the ministry of greeting others.

If you're walking down the hallway and encounter three people standing in a group, it is important to greet each person. It would be both awkward and rude to say hello to one person and ignore the other two. Granted, you may need to talk in depth to one of the three, but first, greet all three and then focus on your conversation with the one.

Likewise, for a moment, think about how awkward it is to actually be in the presence of another human being and not to acknowledge his presence. For instance, think how uncomfortable it is to step into an elevator that another person is already on and to spend several minutes with that person without even acknowledging his presence. It *is* awkward, and I would argue that the awkwardness is not because we don't know this person but because we're both acting as if each other doesn't exist. That's not natural.

Similarly, consider how inappropriate it is to show up at your office, walk past several coworkers, go into your office, and shut the door, without saying a word of greeting to everyone you see. We may think, *I see these people every day, so why should I have to greet them every day?* But it is important to greet everyone, each day.

- When you're being introduced to a family, don't neglect the children.
- When you enter a room with ten people in it, greet each person.

Whenever I teach a seminar, I try to greet as many people as possible before the seminar begins. It's amazing how this simple procedure immediately creates a warm bond between my audience and me. If there are more than fifty people in attendance it may be difficult for me to greet everyone, but the more hands I'm able to shake, the better.

5. Don't neglect greeting people who are a regular part of your daily life.

We may think that it is unnecessary to continually greet people whom we see every day, particularly those with whom we live. We may think, "I see my spouse every day, so why is it important to greet her every time I come home?" But it is important, so we should make an effort to greet them every time we see them. For instance, when returning home from school or work, it's important to greet every family member—individually. When you first arrive at the office, greet all the people you work with—individually.

6. Don't greet people for the wrong reasons.

A primary, underlying premise that applies to all of the One Anothers is the fact that the One Anothers are all about other people, not about us. For instance, we comfort, encourage, accept, and greet others, not for what *we* can get out of it, but for the benefit of others. When we minister the One Anothers, we should have no desire for personal aggrandizement.

And so it is with greeting others.

Years ago, I knew a pastor who had a bad habit of "glad-handing" his constituency. He would try to greet ten to twelve people every sixty seconds. While he was greeting you, he was already looking around for the next person to greet. By chance, if you did get to talk to him for a few minutes, you soon felt that he really wasn't interested in what you had to say; he wanted to work the crowd. I sensed that his motivation for greeting others was self-serving. It wasn't about them; it was all about him.

But I also remember a pastor who, after the service, would give his undivided attention to those who approached him. With determined intent, he would focus on one person at a time. He seemed to be genuinely interested in whatever you had to say.

> A primary, underlying premise that applies to all of the One Anothers is the fact that the One Anothers are all about other people, not about us.

I realize that there needs to be a balance. It would be unproductive to spend ten minutes greeting one person when there are many others who also need to be greeted. But the point I'm making is that our *motivation* for greeting others must be pure and unselfish. Politicians may work the crowd for personal benefit, but we shouldn't.

Jesus said to beware of people who "walk around in flowing robes and love to be greeted in the marketplace" (Luke 20:46).

7. Make eye contact.

When greeting someone, look him in the eye. Eye contact communicates that you are solely focused on him and that he has your undivided attention. Don't try to intimidate someone by staring a hole through him—sometimes too much eye contact can cause someone to feel uncomfortable—but do make eye contact.

8. Smile.

A simple smile is an amazing thing. Although it usually lasts only a few seconds, it sets the stage for a warm, sincere, effective greeting. A smile communicates interest, optimism, hope, joy, and receptivity.

In his book, *How to Win Friends and Influence People*, Dale Carnegie relates these thoughts about the value of a smile:

> It costs nothing, but creates much. It enriches those who receive, without impoverishing those who give. It happens in a flash and the memory of it sometimes lasts forever. None are so rich they can get along without it, and none so poor but are richer for its benefits. It creates happiness in the home, fosters good will in a business, and is the countersign of friends. It is rest to the weary, daylight to the discouraged, sunshine to the sad, and Nature's best antidote for trouble. Yet it cannot be bought, begged, borrowed, or stolen, for it is something that is no earthly good to anybody till it is given away. For nobody needs a smile so much as those who have none left to give![2]

Mr. Carnegie would give his students an interesting assignment: Smile at someone every hour of the day for a week and then come to class and talk about the results. The stories his students told about their experiences were life changing.

Your assignment is similar: When greeting someone—smile. ☺

9. Develop a greeting vocabulary.

Often, we may be reluctant to greet people because we're not sure what to say. That's why we need to learn an appropriate vocabulary. We would benefit from learning several different types of greetings:

- When you don't have a lot of time to spend with someone, and, or, when you're greeting a large group of people one at a time, you might say:
  "Hi, my name is _____, it's good to see you."
  "Hello. I'm so glad you're here."
  "Hi, Jim. Thanks for coming to our home tonight."

- If you are able to spend more time with someone, you might ask about his well-being:
  "Hi, John. How was your day?"
  "Hello, Sarah. How have you been feeling?"

But don't ask questions unless you have the time and the interest to hear and respond to a person's answer. It's rude to ask a person, "How are you doing?" and then walk off before he can answer. If you ask someone a serious question and he senses that you're not really wanting an honest answer, it will just perpetuate dishonest answers and superficial conversation: "Hi, how are you?" "Oh, just fine, how are you?" Such conversation is counterproductive.

10. Call the person by name, or, if you don't know his name, find it out.

The most beautiful sound a person can hear is the sound of her own name. It's imperative that we learn people's names and speak their names frequently. So if you're greeting someone for the first time, ask her name. If you're greeting someone whom you've already met, use her name in your greeting.

But don't ask questions
unless you have the time
and the interest to hear and respond to a person's answer.
It's rude to ask a person, "How are you doing?"
and then walk off before he can answer.

Dale Carnegie, in *How to Win Friends and Influence People*, writes an entire chapter on the importance of knowing and using people's names. He tells this intriguing story about Napoleon the Third.

> Napoleon the Third, Emperor of France and nephew of the great Napoleon, boasted that in spite of all his royal duties he could remember the name of every person he met.
>
> His technique? Simple. If he didn't hear the name distinctly, he said, "So sorry. I didn't get the name clearly." Then, if it was an unusual name, he would say, "How is it spelled?"
>
> During the conversation, he took the trouble to repeat the name several times, and tried to associate it in his mind with the person's features, expressions and general appearance.
>
> If the person was someone of importance, Napoleon went to even further pains. As soon as he was alone, he wrote the name down on a piece of paper, looked at it, concentrated on it, fixed it securely in his mind, and then tore up the paper. In this way he gained an eye impression of the name as well as an ear impression.[3]

So when greeting someone, discover her name quickly, and use her name frequently during the conversation. Third John verse 14 says, "Greet the friends there *by name*" (emphasis added).

11. If you are greeting someone for the first time, give your name.

Not only is it important to discover and use the other person's name, but also insert your own name into the greeting. Sharing your own name is the first step toward being vulnerable with someone and it suggests that you want to establish a relationship.

12. Physically acknowledge and affirm the person.

The apostle Paul would often instruct members of the first-century church to greet one another, not just verbally, but also with a physical gesture: "Greet one another *with a holy kiss*" (Romans 16:16; emphasis added). So when possible and appropriate, our verbal greeting should be accompanied by a physical gesture. Obviously, in the days of Paul, it was culturally appropriate to kiss the cheek of the person who was being greeted. In our culture, a handshake or a pat on the back is the norm. When greeting someone we know well, an embrace is usually appropriate.

Sometimes it will not be possible to physically greet someone. The apostle Paul often greeted the saints through the letters he wrote. Also, social and cultural norms will often dictate whether physical contact is appropriate. But in most situations, Greeting One Another is enhanced by physical involvement.

If sharing your name is the first step toward being vulnerable with someone, initiating physical contact is the next step.

Are you comfortable with physical contact? If not, why?

_____

_____

13. Use a friendly tone of voice, and be warm and personable.

In 1 Corinthians 16:20 we read, "Aquila and Priscilla greet you *warmly* in the Lord" (emphasis added). When greeting someone, our tone of voice and general demeanor should communicate warmth, friendliness and affability. A cold, reserved, reticent, half-hearted greeting is counterproductive.

14. Don't be bothered by "polite conversation."

Most conversations begin with polite, diplomatic themes: "It was a beautiful day today, wasn't it?" "How were your holidays?" "Is John coming home from college next week?" Though everyone knows these topics are generic and somewhat superficial, they are, nevertheless, appropriate and acceptable. There's nothing wrong with being gracious and courteous by engaging in polite conversation. These topics, though predictable and common, usually only last for a few minutes, and they provide a gracious beginning to a conversation and a smooth segue into more serious topics. Even though polite conversation is somewhat superficial, it should never be spoken in a gratuitous manner but with sincerity.

15. Show interest in the person you are greeting.

Once again, let me refer to some insights offered by Dale Carnegie in his book *How to Win Friends and Influence People*. He writes an entire chapter on this one suggestion: Become genuinely interested in other people. He says, "You can make more friends in two months by becoming interested in other people than you can in two years by trying to get other people interested in you. I have discovered from personal experience that one can win the attention, time and cooperation of even the most sought after people by becoming genuinely interested in them."

That's good advice.

Showing interest in a person begins with a sincere attitude: Are you genuinely interested in the person you're greeting, or are you simply patronizing him? Inwardly, do you acknowledge his value as a person and sincerely desire to minister the other One Anothers to him? Most people can sense our motivation behind greeting them; hopefully they will perceive sincerity on our part.

16. If appropriate, introduce the person you are greeting to someone else in the group.

If someone is visiting an organization for the first time or is new to the organization, after greeting this person yourself, introduce him to other people. If possible, stay with the person after you've introduced him to others so he doesn't feel like you "handed him off" and then deserted him. In time, there will probably be a gracious opportunity to leave this person and go to others, but be careful about the transition.

The visitor/new member will be particularly blessed by multiple greetings.

17. If necessary, send greetings via another agent, such as a letter or another person.

A personal greeting is always preferred, but when a face-to-face conversation is impossible or impractical, we can send our greetings through another venue. For instance, the apostle Paul greeted the members of the churches through his letters, often mentioning individuals by name (see Romans 16). Occasionally, Paul would ask someone to greet others on his behalf: "Give my greetings to the brothers at Laodicea" (Colossians 4:15). He was also willing to greet people on behalf of others: "Timothy, my fellow worker, sends his greetings to you" (Romans 16:21).

We live in a technologically advanced society, particularly in the area of telecommunications. We can communicate by phone, pager, fax, and e-mail. Someone has said that if we have more than three ways that people can get in touch with us—we're sick.

While there may be a downside to being so available, why not use modern technology as a tool for greeting one another? At times I will call five to ten of my friends each day, just to greet them and to see how they are doing. It doesn't take a lot of time but the results are significant. A short, personal e-mail can also communicate care and concern.

18. Be sensitive to discern what type of greeting is needed.

B be sensitive to discern how he is feeling emotionally so that we can respond appropriately.

"Like one who takes away a garment on a cold day, or like vinegar poured on soda, is one who sings songs to a heavy heart" (Proverbs 25:20). When greeting someone, we need to be sensitive to discern how he is feeling emotionally so that we can respond appropriately. I once called someone on the telephone and communicated an extremely upbeat, victorious greeting, only to discover that he had just lost a loved one and was in a state of grief. That incident taught me to temper my initial greeting until I can discern the emotional state of the person I'm greeting. This is particularly important when communicating on the telephone because we're not privy to the person's facial expression or body language, both of which can help us discern his feelings.

19. An organization should provide an opportunity and a place for people to greet one another.

Since greeting others is such an important ministry, an organization should provide the time and the place for its constituents to greet one another.

My wife and I have had the opportunity to travel frequently to England for ministry opportunities. They have a wonderful social custom in England called "tea time." At any official gathering of people, time is allocated mid-morning and mid-afternoon for a time of fellowship and gastronomical refreshment. When we first started going to England, I thought it was a waste of time: "Let's stop talking and get down to business." But then I realized that the time provided a perfect venue through which the One Anothers could be ministered. In particular, it was a designated *time* to Greet One Another.

As Mary and I would travel through other parts of Europe, we noticed that most of the towns are built around a plaza or town square. For instance, our favorite town in Italy, Sienna, has a beautiful, cobble-stoned plaza in the middle of town where people can gather to visit. Even late at night, several hundred people will gather to sip cappuccino, walk their dogs, and visit with one another. It is a designated *place* to Greet One Another.

In like manner, we would do well to provide a time and a place for the ministry of greeting to take place. Many churches, as a part of their worship service, include a time of welcoming one another. While this is noble and should be continued, at times it comes across as staged and coerced. After all, when a minister says, "Now, everyone stand up and greet those around you," you really don't have much choice in the matter; some people may even think, *The only reason these people are greeting me is because it would be awkward not to.* While I think this "welcome time" is okay, it does not a friendly church make. People will sense that a church family is genuinely friendly when church members take the initiative to greet them at times that are not orchestrated.

Also, churches should provide a place where greeting can take place. The church I grew up in has a plaza between two buildings that is the unofficial gathering place for the church. Whenever people have a few spare minutes, they head for the plaza where they can meet their friends.

A coffee pot can also help establish a place and opportunity for fellowship. It serves as a magnet for people, not just as a place to quench their thirst but to visit.

Mom's Investment

 ■ While my mother was not an extrovert, she was a very friendly person. She was attracted to people, and people were attracted to her. She was pleasant. She was cordial. She was easy to be around. She never intimidated people by her demeanor, her words, or her actions. ■ She always warmly greeted me. Each day, when I would arrive home from school, she would greet me with a smile and a kiss. Even when I was away at college, when I came home for holidays, she would anticipate my arrival time and be sitting on the front porch, waiting for me to pull up in the driveway. She always offered a refreshing drink and perhaps some cookies. ■ All my life, I sensed that Mom delighted in seeing me. Even after I was married and left home, I always felt that I was welcome in her house. ■ Thanks, Mom.

Write your own definition of Greet One Another.

_____

_____

_____

Personal Journal

1. Write about a person you know, who has continually blessed you by greeting you on a regular basis. _____
_____

2. Does greeting others come naturally for you or is it a struggle? Why? _____
_____

3. Do you tend to be a "get-it-done" type person? If so, do you ever struggle with prioritizing people over projects, agendas, and deadlines? _____
_____

4. Are you hesitant to look people in the eyes? Why? _____
_____

5. How often do you smile? It's been said that it takes seventy-two muscles to frown and only fourteen to smile. Do you agree with this? _____
_____

6. How often do you send a greeting via a letter, phone call, or e-mail?
_____
_____

7. What can you do this week to greet your two secret recipients?
Secret recipient _____
Unchurched secret recipient _____

8. On a scale from 1 to 10 (1 being, "I need to greatly improve" and 10 being, "I do a good job"), how well do you do at greeting others? Ask your OA Partner to rate you.

I rated myself a _____.
My OA partner rated me a _____.

Practical Suggestion #3

We should initiate giving the One Anothers and minister them with enthusiasm.

In 2 Corinthians 8:17, Paul commended Titus for his enthusiasm and his initiative: "I thank God, who put into the heart of Titus the same concern I have for you. For Titus not only welcomed our appeal, but he is coming to you with much *enthusiasm* and on his own *initiative*" (emphasis added). (Also, see 2 Corinthians 9:2).

As we study each of the One Anothers, we'll notice that the issue of initiative is very important. In other words, who initiates the transaction? Should I wait until someone asks for comfort before I comfort him? Should people have to request support before I offer it? No. We should be sensitive to notice when someone has a need and then be proactive in meeting it. While there's nothing wrong with responding to a specific requests—"I really had a tough day, can I talk to you about it?"—people are particularly blessed when we anticipate and notice times when they need to be ministered to—"I can tell you've had a hard day, let's talk."

John 3:16 states that God so loved the world that he sent Jesus. Notice that God took the initiative. The apostle John says the same thing, in a different way, in 1 John 4:19, "We love because he first loved us."

The issue of initiative is easily applicable to each of the One Anothers:

- Don't wait for your offender to ask for forgiveness—forgive him!
- Don't be apathetic regarding someone's hurt and pain—comfort her!
- Don't wait for someone to ask for encouragement—encourage him!
- Don't wait until someone becomes overwhelmed—bear her burden!
- Don't wait for someone to greet you—greet him!

Equally important is the issue of enthusiasm. Are we ministering to others out of a sense of duty and obligation or out of gratitude and enthusiasm? Will we Prefer One Another grudgingly or with enthusiasm? Will we Serve One Another reluctantly, out of compulsion, or will we serve people joyfully? Will we Offer Hospitality to One Another simply because we're the social chairman of our Bible study group and it's our responsibility, or because we enjoy blessing other people? People can usually tell the difference.

In 2 Corinthians 9:7, we learn that God loves a *cheerful* giver. God's not the only one who delights in cheerful giving; we all are blessed when someone gives passionately and earnestly. The combination of initiative and enthusiasm is powerful. We need to incorporate both into our ministry to others.

Write about a time this last week that you initiated ministering one of the One Anothers.

_____

_____

_____

Write about a time this last week when someone initiated giving one of the One Anothers to you.

_____

_____

_____

Why is it important to be enthusiastic and cheerful whenever we minister the One Anothers?

_____

_____

_____

Powerful Result #3

As we consistently minister the One Anothers, love will increase and unity will be developed among the body of Christ.

In 2 Thessalonians 1:3, Paul commended the Thessalonians because "the love every one of you has for each other is increasing." Our love for other people is dynamic—it can grow and prosper, or it can wane and become anemic. By regularly practicing the One Anothers, we maintain a growing love for others.

- Increasingly, I am more conscious of the fact that people (including myself) need the One Anothers.
- Increasingly, I have a deep desire to give the One Anothers to other people.
- Increasingly, I have developed the necessary skills to minister the One Anothers; I notice when people need each particular one, and I am willing to take the time to give to others.

Furthermore, the One Anothers are one key element in producing and maintaining unity among the body of Christ. In 1 Corinthians 12:25, the apostle Paul states that "there should be no division in the body, but … its parts should have equal concern for each other." Among any group of people, one of the best ways to develop unity and to guard against division is to increase the level of care that people have for one another. Even differences and disagreements are more easily managed when genuine care is expressed. The old adage "I don't care how much you know until I know how much you care" is true.

I have a sermon called "When It's Better Not to Go to Church" which is based on 1 Corinthians 11:17-22. Read the passage and notice that the Corinthian church suffered from divisions within the body. Then, imagine how the One Anothers would have solved all of the problems they were experiencing.

Describe one of your relationships in which "love is increasing." What is prompting this increase?

_____

_____

Group Time—Session Four

Each member of the group should give his or her individual response to the first three questions. Allow about two minutes for each person's response. Allow all group members to share their answer to question #1 before proceeding to question #2.

1. What was the most interesting concept in this chapter?
2. Referring back to last week's lesson, share about a time this week when you were able to accept someone else and a time when you should have accepted someone else but did not.
3. Share your responses to the first three Personal Journal entries in this chapter (page 56).

As a group, process these discussion questions: [These discussion questions have been prioritized. Depending on the time allotted for your group discussion, you may not be able to process all the questions.]

   a. Is being shy a good excuse for not greeting others?
   b. When is it a challenge to greet others? (e.g., when we're feeling bad, in a new environment, or with people with whom there is unresolved hurt.)
   c. What can you do when you greet someone and he snubs you?
   d. How should we *receive* a greeting?
   e. How will greeting other people be a testimony to "all men" (John 13:34) that we belong to the Lord and that we are his disciples?
   f. Why is it important to greet people *by name*? Share some tips on how you remember people's names.
   g. Does your organization provide a *time* and *place* for people to greet each other? If yes, how can it be improved? If not, how can such a place and time be provided?
   h. On a scale from 1 to 10 (1 being, "We're not too good at this" and 10 being, "We're really good at this"), how good is your church/organization at greeting people?

Homework:
Read and process chapter 5.

ENCOURAGE ONE ANOTHER

"Encourage one another" (1 Thessalonians 5:11).

Years ago, Pepper Rodgers was having a terrible season as head coach at UCLA. He was getting a lot of criticism from the press and alumni, and even his wife, a true-blue Bruins fan, was getting impatient. Reflecting back on that difficult time in his life, Pepper said, "My dog was my only friend. I told my wife that a man needs at least two friends, and she bought me another dog."[1]

Pepper needed a generous dose of encouragement.

The most frequently mentioned One Another in the Bible is Encourage One Another. Perhaps it is the most needed, the one ministry that we need on a consistent, continuous basis. Indeed, Hebrews 3:13 instructs us to "encourage one another daily."

There are many different reasons why we need to encourage others.

1. **Encourage people when they're discouraged.**

    Encouragement gives courage, hope, and emotional strength to someone who is struggling.

    Jesus said, "In this world you will have problems." That wasn't a threat, just a statement of fact, perhaps even a warning. Life is tough. Disappointments come, things break, and relationships turn sour. When problems come, discouragement is usually close behind, and when it casts a heavy shadow upon us, we need a good dose of encouragement.

    When we are going through difficult times, we are particularly susceptible to thoughts of unbelief—"Why is God allowing this to happen? Does he even care? Does he even exist?" Encouragement is an antidote for these struggles. "See to it, brothers, that none of you has a sinful, unbelieving heart that turns away from the living God. But encourage one another daily, as long as it is called Today, so that none of you may be hardened by sin's deceitfulness" (Hebrews 3:12–13).

    Describe a time in your life when you were particularly discouraged. Did anyone encourage you?

    _____

    _____

Think of someone you know who is discouraged. How could you encourage him?

_____

_____

2. **Encourage people when they have become "weary in well doing."**

Encouragement strengthens and reinforces someone who is on the right course.

We often need encouragement, not because things are going wrong, but because we're just tired of doing that which is right. Even that which is honorable and good can, in time, become mundane and laborious. Galatians 6:9 calls it becoming "weary in doing good."

Have you ever considered the job description of a commercial airline pilot? "Years of tedious boredom punctuated by moments of stark terror."

For most people, life has a similar cycle—years of routine, predictable living, interrupted by infrequent burst of invigorating, challenging experiences. Those short periods of transition, while filled with a degree of anxiety, are also exciting and stimulating. Graduation from a particular level of schooling (elementary, high school, college), getting married, the birth of a child, moving to a new house, career changes—these are times of high interest.

But what about the "in-between times," the years of tedious boredom? The "middle years" of college (sophomore and junior years), years of changing diapers, going to the same office year after year, hearing the same preacher for ten years, cleaning the house—again.

Have you ever considered the job description of
a commercial airline pilot? "Years of tedious
boredom punctuated by moments of stark terror."

And what about the potential weariness of maintaining personal convictions and acts of kindness—maintaining moral purity in the midst of a perverse society, continuing to pay taxes on cash income, hours of unselfish service at the local hospital, serving in Vacation Bible School—one more year?

To make it through these "plodding" periods, we need to be encouraged.

Describe a time in your life when you became "weary in well doing." Did anyone encourage you?

_____

_____

Think of someone you know who may be tired of doing that which is good. How could you encourage this person?

_____

_____

3. Encourage people when they seem to be unfocused, confused, or unmotivated.

Encouragement persuades someone toward that which is good and desirable and stimulates toward honorable goals.

Have you ever been stuck in a rut? I'm not talking about the kind that makes for a great sales pitch for SUVs. I'm talking about more significant challenges:

- Physically—"I can't seem to lose weight." "I sleep too much."
- Emotionally—"I can't seem to get over my divorce." "I have a hard time getting close to anyone."
- Vocationally—"I've been working the same job for years; I'm stuck." "I can't decide what to do after I graduate from college."
- Spiritually—"I'm so complacent about my walk with the Lord. I'm not sure what I believe anymore."
- Financially—"I'm getting deeper and deeper into debt. My finances are a mess."
- Relationally—"My marriage is hurting." "My kids are going ballistic." "My sister won't speak to me."

It's usually hard to get out of a rut *alone*. We need a push, a fresh idea, someone to come alongside us and to give us aid. We need encouragement.

Describe a time in your life when you were in a rut. Did someone offer to help you?

_____

_____

Think of someone you know that may be "stuck" and in need of some help. How could you minister to him?

_____

_____

4. Encourage people to dream and to take bold initiatives.

Encouragement inspires others with courage, spirit, and hope.

In 1805, Haydn, the great composer, was seventy-three years old. In that year, at Vienna, he met, for the first time, the future musical artist Cherubini, who was thirty years Haydn's junior, and who had not yet become famous for his compositions. Haydn, however, saw promise in the younger man and paid him one of the most gracious compliments an older and established musician could offer to a younger and still unmade artist. Haydn handed Cherubini one of his latest compositions and remarked: "Permit me to style myself your musical father, and to call you my son." Cherubini was so impressed that he could not keep back the tears as he took leave of the old man. With one act of kindness, Haydn had inspired Cherubini to pursue his dreams and to reach his potential.[2]

Most people have an unwritten "dream list"—ideas and plans that appear to be beyond reach but remain in their hearts nevertheless:

- "I want to write a book."
- "I want to travel to Europe."
- "I want to start my own business."
- "I want to finish a college degree."

The pursuit of these seemingly impossible dreams can often be jump-started by encouragement. Young people particularly need to be encouraged to pursue their dreams.

What are some things you have always wanted to do but have never done?

_____

Think of someone you know who has a dream that is yet to be fulfilled. What could you do to help her achieve this dream?

_____

5. **Encourage people in their pursuit of godly character.**

Encouragement persuades people to live godly lives and develop godly character.

In Titus 2:6, Paul told Titus to "encourage the young men to be self-controlled." We should continually encourage others to live godly lives and to develop godly character. For instance, we can:

- Encourage people to resist evil when they are tempted.
- Encourage people to aspire to godly character traits (loyalty, dependability, reverence, punctuality, etc.).
- Encourage people to pursue holiness.

Describe a time when someone encouraged you toward godliness and away from evil.

_____

_____

Think of someone you know who might need encouraging in this way and write down how you could encourage this person.

_____

_____

An Example of Encouragement

Mrs. Newbury loved her fifth-grade students. Her concern for them went far beyond her professional duty to teach them academics. She cared about their personal lives—how they felt about themselves.

One year, her students started to tease each other, and she was afraid that only the strong would survive. She devised a plan to try to reverse the trend.

One morning she handed each student a piece of paper that had only the name of a fellow classmate written at the top. Her instruction was simple: "I want you to write down the things you appreciate most about this person, the things that make this person special."

When the students were through writing, Mrs. Newbury did a wise thing. "Now turn your papers into me," she said. "I'll type them up tonight; that way no one will know who wrote what." That evening she was able to edit each piece, removing comments that would not be complimentary, adding comments when necessary to ensure that each student had a long list.

The next day she gave the students their personalized lists. The impact was immediate—this good dose of appreciation and encouragement changed the spirit of the entire class.

The exercise worked so well she decided to make it a yearly event. Year after year kids were affirmed and encouraged.

Years later, Mrs. Newbury died. As expected, many former students returned to attend the memorial service of the teacher who so deeply impacted their lives.

At the graveside, several former students began to talk, and the conversation inevitably included the then famous exercise of writing words of encouragement.

One tall man, now a distinguished businessman, remarked, "I'm kind of embarrassed to admit this, but I've been carrying my piece of paper all through the years." He opened his wallet, took out a well-creased piece of paper, and said, "I can't tell you how many times I've read this through the years. If it hadn't been for these words of encouragement, I'm not sure if I would have made it through the tough times."

A woman, having gained confidence from the businessman's honesty and vulnerability, shared, "It had the same impact on me." As she pulled her piece of paper from her purse, she read aloud one of the sentences, "Linda, I appreciate you that you are always sensitive to people when they're hurting. You're really special." Then she shared with the group, "Those words of encouragement were partly why I became a nurse."

Another man said, "I don't have mine with me, but it's under the glass top of my desk at the office."

Many others testified of the life-changing impact of those notes of encouragement.

I have my own Mrs. Newbury story. His name was Lee Roy Till.

Lee Roy was the minister of music at my home church. When I am asked to list the men who have impacted me the most in life, his name is always at, or near, the top of the list. Although he was only a direct part of my life for about six years (my junior high and high school years), his life and ministry touched me deeply. Thirty years later, I can still remember specific words he said and how he reacted to various situations. (This should put holy fear in those of us who are in a position to influence children and students.)

> "I'm kind of embarrassed to admit this, but I've been carrying my piece of paper all through the years. I can't tell you how many times I've read this through the years. If it hadn't been for these words of encouragement, I'm not sure if I would have made it through the tough times."

My senior year in high school I was elected president of our youth choir, which was a really big deal. I served to the best of my ability, and at the end of the year Lee Roy gave me a thank-you gift: a leather-bound copy of the Bible, red-letter edition.

Although I was blessed by the gift itself, it was what Lee Roy wrote on the inside cover that affected me so deeply. Being an impressionable seventeen-year-old boy who desperately needed approval and affirmation, his inspired words written solely to me, encouraged me as much at that moment, as the inspired words contained in the sixty-six books of the Bible.

Mr. Till wrote:

Dear Don,

Your leadership as president of the Chapel Choir this past year has been outstanding. If I had to pick one area of leadership where you especially excelled, it would be in the area of most importance—that of the spiritual preparation of the choir.

God has endowed you with many talents, I am grateful to him for you and your dedication to his service.

May you always know and follow God's direction for your life. He has great things in store for you, and I have the confidence to believe you will claim each for his glory.

I count it a very personal blessing to know and serve with you. I will be following your future with great personal interest. You will be in my prayers.
God bless you always and in all ways.
Sincerely in Christ,
Lee Roy Till

I would read Lee Roy's gracious words over and over. God used his words to affirm God's plan for my life. A year later, I committed my life to the gospel ministry and was ordained (*May you always know and follow God's direction for your life*). Ten years later, I finished a Ph.D. degree (*God has endowed you with many talents*). I have served the Lord faithfully for thirty years (*I will be following your future with great personal interest*). Some have commented through the years that my ministry seems to focus on the most "important thing"—the spiritual (*If I had to pick one area of leadership where you especially excelled, it would be in the area of most importance—that of the spiritual preparation of the choir*). I have always had a sense of destiny about my life (*He has great things in store for you*). I seem to have a courageous, "can-do" attitude (*I have the confidence to believe you will claim each for his glory*).

Am I making too much of this incident? I don't think so. It probably was not *the* defining moment in my life, but I don't think there was just one. My life has been shaped more by defining *moments*, a collection of events and incidences in which an intense dose of one of the One Anothers was applied to my very needy soul at just the right time.

Do you remember the words to the song made famous by Diane Warwick, "What the world needs now, is love, sweet love"? Truer words have never been sung. Remember, we can substitute any of the One Anothers whenever we see the word *love*. As I reflect back on my life, I'm grateful that Lee Roy, along with many people, gave me "encouragement, sweet encouragement."

We should make it our mission in life that we will be a constant source of encouragement to those around us.

The "ministry of your presence" can make a *powerful statement.*

Practical Ways to Encourage One Another

1. Learn to sense when other people need to be encouraged. At the beginning of this chapter, I listed five reasons that people need to be encouraged. Become adept at recognizing when people are experiencing one or more of these times and be available to help them.

2. We can encourage others by sharing a personal testimony of the work of God in our lives. For instance, in Acts 16:40, Paul and Silas encouraged the church by sharing with them how God delivered them from prison.

3. Sometimes, we need to encourage people on a daily basis (Hebrews 3:13).

4. We can encourage others by teaching sound doctrine (Titus 1:9).

5. We can encourage others by our example. In Titus 2:6–8, Paul tells Titus to encourage the young men through his integrity, seriousness, and soundness of speech.

6. Encourage with authority (Titus 2:15). Don't be reticent or apologetic, and don't worry about whether or not encouraging others looks "cool."

7. Encourage each other with hope (1 Thessalonians 4:17–18). Hope is future-oriented, so we can encourage others by sharing thoughts about anticipated, positive, future events. For instance, in 1 Thessalonians 4:17–18, Paul encourages believers by sharing about the future coming of the Lord. A struggling college student could be encouraged by thoughts of graduation and post-college life.

8. Learn how to speak words of encouragement (1 Thessalonians 4:18).

9. Often, just our presence will encourage others. The "ministry of your presence" can make a powerful statement. Your presence at a recital, sporting event, or funeral service will serve as a potent ministry of encouragement.

10. Other ways to encourage would include: giving a physical or financial gift, defending someone, taking time to listen, demonstrating appropriate body language (a smile or hug), sharing a truthful and believable compliment, inquiring as to how someone is progressing toward a goal, praying with and for someone, making an unexpected phone call, and sharing a pertinent verse of Scripture.

11. Encourage others to set goals, and then help them achieve them. Also, encourage others to live productive lives by helping them develop God-given plans and goals and then become actively involved in helping them reach those goals (Hebrews 10:24). Psalm 64:5 speaks of those who "encourage each other in evil plans"; we should encourage one another in godly plans.

Mom's Investment

 ■ When I was a kid, we lived a few blocks from Five Mile Creek, which was the delightful playground for neighborhood adventurers. Many a summer day was spent exploring, fishing, and acting out whatever TV show we had seen the night before. ■ One summer, I must have just seen the movie *Huckleberry Finn* because I had a dream to build a raft, pack some supplies, and then spend several days sailing down Five Mile Creek. ■ Back in the "old days," fruits and vegetables were shipped in wooden crates. We lived only a few blocks from a grocery store, so for days I raided the trash dumpster, collecting all the spare crates and other materials necessary to build a world-class, seaworthy vessel. ■ With no architectural plan other than my imagination, I began to assemble the materials into a six-by-eight-foot raft. I realized that even though the raft was made of wood it would need extra buoyancy, so I collected coffee cans from all the neighbors and nailed them to the bottom of the raft. ■ The day of the maiden voyage arrived. Mom helped me pack some food and water for the journey, and after a prayer, I was off. ■ Only then did I realize that the raft was too cumbersome and heavy for me to get it to the creek by myself. ■ I solicited Mom's help. ■ I'll never forget those next moments. Even forty years later they are vivid. ■ First, let me set the context. It was summertime in Texas; it was hot. Although we lived close to the creek, there were no sidewalks, and the final descent to the creek was perilously steep. My mom, though no engineer herself, knew the raft would never float. ■ But despite all the reasons not to make the journey, my mother, with eager enthusiasm, helped me drag the raft to its inevitable destiny. ■ I remember that mom wore a dress that day, not the ideal outfit for an adventurous outing. I remember that while dragging the raft toward the creek it would get stuck and we would have to lift it off the ground to free it. I remember having to negotiate the steep incline toward the bank. Mom went first. ■ And all the while, Mom was encouraging me. "Bo [my nickname], this is a wonderful raft. I'm so proud of you for building it. You may get to the Gulf of Mexico by nighttime." ▦ All the while, she knew that the raft would not float. ▦ When we finally got to the creek bank, we slid the raft into the water, and it continued to follow the contour of the land. It sank fast. ▦ I was devastated. ▦ But Mom was there to encourage me. "Bo, it's still a wonderful raft. We [notice the plural pronoun] must have just forgotten to do something." ▦ Her words breathed new life into the death of a vision. With hopeful enthusiasm I commented, "Let's take it back to the garage, and I can fix it!" ▦ My mother smiled and then grabbed the rope. ▦ We thought the trip down to the creek was tough; going back was worse. We finally made it back to the house. I ran off to play with my friends, and Mom probably collapsed in bed. The following week I must have seen *Swiss Family Robinson* because I was no longer interested in rafts, now it was tree houses. ▦ I have often reflected back on the raft incident. First, why do I remember it so well? Why are the details etched so accurately in my mind? I believe it is because it was a life-shaping event. It was a phenomenal deposit in the bank of my soul of the One Another called encouragement. ▦ Throughout my life, I've always had an ample amount of creativity—an entrepreneurial, "can-do" attitude. Though probably present in my soul from birth, perhaps it was "coming out" during the conception and building stages of the raft project and solidified that day on the journey to Five Mile Creek. ▦ What if my mother had said, "Bo, that raft isn't going to float ... I'm too busy to help you drag that thing down to the creek ... I just took a bath, and I've got a dress on ... You're always coming up with some new hair-brain project." Perhaps my creative genes would have been forever dormant. ▦ But she didn't. ▦ Instead, she encouraged me. And her encouragement helped positively shape my life. ▦ Thanks, Mom.

Write your own definition of Encourage One Another.

_____

_____

_____

Personal Journal

1. Write about a time in your life when someone significantly encouraged you.

   _____

2. Write about the last time you encouraged someone else.

   _____

3. Write about a time when you observed someone else encouraging another person.

   _____

4. Hebrews 3:13 tells us to encourage one another *daily*. Obviously, we are not around all of our friends on a daily basis, but most of us do have family members and friends whom we do see daily. List the people you interact with the most.

   _____

   Do you have a ministry of "daily encouragement" to these people? Would you be willing to commit to this steady, consistent ministry?

5. There are certain individuals (and perhaps even certain personality types) who may need extra doses of encouragement. For instance, Paul said to, "Encourage the timid" (1 Thessalonians 5:14). Also, everyone goes through periods of life during which encouragement is a priority need (after a real or perceived failure or during transitions, financial struggles, physical challenges, etc.), and some individuals, because of their place in life, have special needs (such as the elderly, widows, single parents, and Christian leaders/activists).

   List several people you are close to who seem to just need a lot of encouragement on an ongoing basis.

   _____, _____, _____.

   List several people you are close to who are currently going through a challenging situation.

   _____, _____, _____.

   List several people who may need encouragement because of their places in life.

   _____, _____, _____.

   In the next few days, how could you encourage these people?

   _____

6. Encouragement is one of the spiritual gifts listed in Romans 12 (v. 8). This simply means that some believers are particularly inclined to encourage others and have been specially gifted to do so. We should observe their administration of this gift and learn from them.

   List several people whom you know who might have the gift of encouragement. As you observe them encouraging others, what can you learn from them about the ministry of encouragement?

   Name _____

   What I can learn _____

   Name _____

   What I can learn _____

7. A good way to encourage people is by writing personal notes. If you don't already have some, purchase note cards and try to write several notes of encouragement every week.

   This week, I will write a note of encouragement to: _____,
   _____, _____, and _____.

8. What can you do this week to encourage your two secret recipients?

   Secret Recipient _____
   Unchurched recipient _____

9. On a scale from 1 to 10 (1 being, "I need to greatly improve" and 10 being, "I do a good job"), how well do you encourage others? Ask your OA Partner to rate you.

   I rated myself a _____.
   My OA partner rated me a _____.

Practical Suggestion #4
Focus on giving the One Anothers to one person at a time.

The phrase "one another" suggests that all thirty-five One Anothers are best ministered to one person at a time—one person giving to another person, not one person to a group.

At times, the One Anothers can be ministered to a group of people. It's common for a public speaker to warmly greet his entire audience, a minister to comfort the entire congregation at a funeral, or a schoolteacher to show hospitality to her entire class. But as a general rule, the One Anothers are most effective when ministered one on one.

Those of us who are in a position of ministry leadership often get trapped into a "herd mentality." Our ministries can become so large that we begin to think that we simply can't keep in personal touch with every member, so we inadvertently neglect any one-on-one ministry. To avoid showing favoritism to a few, we focus solely on the masses. There are several dangers to this.

First, *it removes us from the frontline "trenches" of ministry*. We can become so involved in organizing ministry that we lose touch with hurting people. But Jesus always found time to minister to individuals. Yes, at times he taught thousands, but every day he touched people one at a time. If Jesus had the time and the propensity for individual ministry, so should we.

Second, *when we only minister to the masses, we run the risk of removing ourselves from the accountability of actually living the gospel*. We end up talking about the gospel but not walking it. First Corinthians 4:20 says that "the kingdom of God is not a matter of talk but of power." Ministry-wise, the One Anothers are part of the "power" of the kingdom; they challenge us to walk our talk. Notice that all the One

Anothers are active verbs; they are something you *do*.

Another reason we need to minister one-to-one is that *every person is different and has different needs*. For instance, let's imagine that you have five children, ranging in ages from four to eighteen. One evening you're in the den when all five children enter the room. Which One Another is needed at that moment? There are probably five different answers.

- Johnny (age four) needs to be *greeted* because he's feeling left out.
- Sarah (age eight) needs *acceptance* because she felt like a failure at school today.
- Jennifer (age eleven) needs for someone to *carry her burden* because she has a science fair project due tomorrow.
- Randall (age fourteen) needs *comfort* because he found out today that he didn't make the baseball team.
- Norman (age eighteen) needs to be *admonished* because he just used the car without getting permission.

In this situation, to minister effectively, you must minister to each child individually. Sound complicated and time consuming? It is. That's why becoming a parent is such a serious and time-consuming commitment.

In his earthly ministry, Jesus prioritized the importance of ministering just to one person. He told three consecutive parables (recorded in Luke 15) that emphasize the priority of pursuing the one. He told of a shepherd who had one hundred sheep, lost one of them, left

71

the ninety-nine out in the open country, and went and searched for the one lost sheep. Mathematically, the story doesn't make much sense. What if, while the shepherd was looking for the one, ten other sheep had wandered off or been attacked by wolves? But the moral of the parable is not about percentages; the story illustrates the burden of the shepherd (who represents God the Father) for the one. The second parable is about a woman who had ten coins but lost one. She went to a lot of trouble to find the lost coin; when she found it, she rejoiced greatly. The third parable is the story of the prodigal son. A father's youngest son spends his inheritance on riotous living and yet is accepted back into his father's house. Notice that all three stories end with a party. There is great rejoicing over the one sheep, coin, and son that were found.

There are a lot of lessons to learn in these stories, but the one I see most clearly is that God is interested in the individual, whatever effort it takes to minister to just one person is worth it, and that he rejoices greatly over singular acts of ministry.

We will experience a deep dimension of joy in ministry when we minister to individuals. I often speak before large crowds and enjoy doing so. But that does not compare to the joy of holding my wife in my arms and comforting her. Likewise, it's invigorating to plan big events and see them come to fruition. But I am actually more fulfilled when I hug a child at church and tell her how special she is. Yes, there is great joy and fulfillment in giving the One Anothers—to one person at a time.

Shortly before daybreak, a man strolled down the shore of a beach. As he strolled, he saw that the beach was covered with starfish that had been thrown ashore and helplessly stranded by the great waves. Once the morning sun shone through the clouds, the starfish would dry out and die.

Suddenly the man saw an interesting sight. A young boy who had also noticed the plight of the starfish was picking them up, one at a time, and flinging them back into the ocean.

"Why are you doing that?" the man asked the lad as he got close enough to be heard. "Can't you see that one person will never make a difference—you'll never be able to get all those starfish back into the water. There are just too many."

"Yes, that's true," the boy sighed as he bent over and picked up another and tossed it back into the water. Then as he watched it sink, he looked at the man, smiled, and said, "But it sure made a difference to that one."[3]

Powerful Result #4

As we continually share the One Anothers, our lives will be built on solid ground.

Those of us who grew up going to church are probably familiar with the story about the wise and foolish builders (Matthew 7:24–27). We even learned a song that helped etch the parable on our minds:

> The wise man built his house upon the rock.
> And the rain came tumbling down.
> The rains came down and the floods came up.
> And the house on the rock stood firm.
>
> The foolish man built his house upon the sand.
> And the rain came tumbling down.
> The rains came down and the floods went up.
> And the house on the sand went "crash."

Fun song; interesting parable. But few of us remember the moral of the story. Most of us do remember that the two houses represent two different lives and that the fierce rains and wind represent the storms of life that inevitably assail our lives. But do you remember what the story is teaching? What distinguished the wise builder from the foolish one? Looking to the text we read, "Therefore everyone who hears these words of mine and *puts them into practice* is like a wise man" (v. 24; emphasis added). "But everyone who hears these words of mine and *does not put them into practice* is like a foolish man" (v. 26; emphasis added).

This parable is not differentiating between a believer and an unbeliever, nor is it contrasting those who are disciplined students of the Bible with casual readers. The sole difference is on the phrase "puts them into practice." The emphasis is on *doing* the truth. Essentially, the Lord is saying that simply knowing the truth is not enough; our lives will be firmly grounded only as we *do* the Word.

Through more than thirty years of ministry, I have observed the truth of this parable personified in the lives of many believers. I've watched Bible-believing people—people who faithfully attend church, who believe right, who honor God with their lips, sincere people—fall apart when the hurricanes of life strike. I've also watched believers traverse incredibly difficult passages of life with their lives remaining intact. If we were to run a statistical analysis of variance, the one variable that would prove to be statistically significant would be: "Therefore everyone who hears these words of mine and *puts them into practice* is like a wise man" (v. 24; emphasis added). According to Jesus' teaching, the main difference between believers who make it through tough times with their faith intact and those who don't is the "doing the Word" issue.

That's yet another reason the ministry of the One Anothers is so critical. This workbook focuses on *doing* what the Word has commanded us to do. To embrace the truth in our minds is insufficient; even for the truth to take the eighteen-inch plunge to our hearts is inadequate. Truth needs to influence our hands, feet, and lips.

As we faithfully and consistently minister the One Anothers, our lives will be fortified and strengthened.

Group Time—Session Five

Each member of the group should give his or her individual response to the first three questions. Allow about two minutes for each person's response. Allow all group members to share their answer to question #1 before proceeding to question #2.

1. What was the most interesting concept in this chapter?

2. Referring back to last week's lesson, share about a time this week when you were able to greet someone else and a time when you should have greeted someone else but did not.

3. Share your responses to the first three Personal Journal entries in this chapter (page 69).

As a group, process these discussion questions. [These discussion questions have been prioritized. Depending on the time allotted for your group discussion, you may not be able to process all the questions.]

    a.   In Hebrews 10:25, we are told, "Let us not give up meeting together, as some are in the habit of doing, but let us encourage one another." This is basically an admonition to be faithful to attend church connected to an admonition to encourage one another. Why the connection? Could it be that the ministry of encouragement should be one of the primary functions of a church? Could it be that one reason these believers were reluctant to meet together is because there wasn't much encouragement being dispensed when they did meet together?

    b.   Romans 15:4 teaches that the Scriptures will encourage us and that the Word of God will bring us hope. "For everything that was written in the past was written to teach us, so that through endurance and the encouragement of the Scriptures we might have hope." Share a time in your life when God's Word encouraged you. How did it give you hope?

    c.   On several occasions, Paul sent his friend, Tychicus, to visit certain groups of people for the expressed purpose of encouraging them. He sent him to the church at Ephesus for that specific reason (Ephesians 6:22) and to the church at Colosse (Colossians 4:8). The ministry of encouragement can and should be a distinct ministry from one person or group of people to another. At times an encouraging emissary can be sent. How could this truth become a part of the ministry of an organization? For instance, a Bible study group, as part of its ongoing ministry, could periodically commission an individual in the group or several members of the group to go on an "encouragement assignment."

    d.   It's easier to encourage people when they are vulnerable about their needs. But before people will be transparent and open about their needs, they must sense that they have a "safe place" in which to share. How can we as individuals become "safe places"? How can our organizations become "safe places"?

    e.   How will encouraging other people be a testimony to "all men" (John 13:34) that we belong to the Lord and that we are his disciples?

    f.   On a scale from 1 to 10 (1 being, "We're not too good at this" and 10 being, "We're really good at this"), how good is your church/organization at encouraging people?

Homework:
Read and process chapter 6.

COMFORT ONE ANOTHER

"Comfort those in any trouble" (2 Corinthians 1:4).

"Where have you been?" the mother demanded.

The little girl replied, "On my way home I met a friend who was crying because she had broken her doll."

"Oh," said her mother, "then you stopped to help her fix the doll?"

"Oh, no," replied the little girl, "I stopped to help her cry."[1]

In John 16:33, Jesus said, "In this world you will have trouble." It's not a matter of *if* we're going to be hurt, but rather *when* we will be hurt and more importantly, what are we going to do about it? Jesus' statement was not a threat, just a statement of fact. Hurt and pain are inevitable in life and only one thing will bring true relief—comfort.

To comfort is to come alongside someone when they are distressed, to respond to a hurting person with words, feelings, and touch—to hurt with and for another person's pain.

Hurt can take many forms: "I feel ... betrayed, frustrated, embarrassed, lonely, deceived, disappointed, afraid, grieved, irritable, humiliated, apprehensive" but the antidote is always the same—comfort.

While some hurts may be perceived as relatively minor ("I spilt ketchup on my shirt.") and some major ("I lost my job today."), all hurts need to be comforted.

Pastor Jess Moody said this about compassion, "Compassion is not a snob gone slumming. Anybody can salve his conscience by an occasional foray into knitting for the spastic home. Did you ever take a *real* trip down inside the broken heart of a friend? To feel the sob of the soul—the raw, red crucible of emotional agony? To have this become almost as much yours as that of your soul-crushed neighbor? Then, to sit down with him—and silently weep? This is the beginning of compassion."

One particular phrase of Moody's commentary on compassion is particularly poignant—"to have this become almost as much yours as that of your soul-crushed neighbor." There is a significant difference between sympathy and empathy. The former is mainly a mental exercise that says, "I understand that you are hurting." Empathy (and true comfort) goes one step further: "I am hurting that you are hurting." Comfort involves entering into the emotional pain of another person—to actually feel as another person feels.

It's important to create a "comforting environment"—a safe place where people can share their hurt, confident that they will receive comfort. Our churches should be safe places for hurting people, but often we communicate intolerance toward those who are hurting. Likewise, our individual lives should become "safe places." People should sense that when they share their hurts with us, we will properly respond to them.

A profound example of genuine comfort is recorded in the eleventh chapter of John's Gospel. It is the story of Jesus raising Lazarus from the dead.

There were two miracles that day in Bethany:
Lazarus was raised from the dead,
and God cried.

Lazarus and his two sisters, Mary and Martha, were close friends of Jesus. He would often visit their home in Bethany for fellowship and refreshment.

Lazarus becomes ill, and Jesus is summoned to help. When Jesus finally arrives, Lazarus has been dead for four days. Jesus is planning on raising Lazarus from the dead because he says, "Our friend Lazarus has fallen asleep; but I am going there to wake him up" (v. 11).

When Jesus arrives, Mary and Martha are at the grave of their deceased brother, still mourning his death. Verse 33 says, "When Jesus saw her weeping, and the Jews who had come along with her also weeping, he was deeply moved in his spirit and troubled."

Then comes the shortest verse in the Bible: "Jesus wept."

It's important to understand *why* Jesus was weeping. He was not crying because Lazarus was dead; he had already declared that he would live again. Jesus was weeping because his friends were weeping. He was empathizing with their sorrow.

Just think of what Jesus *could* have said at this point: "Mary, don't cry; I'm going to raise your brother from the dead." And this statement would have been absolutely true. But he didn't say anything. He just cried.

There were two miracles that day in Bethany:

Lazarus was raised from the dead,

and God cried.

Practical Ways to Comfort One Another

1. **Learn to sense when people need comfort and be available and willing to minister to them.**

    While we should be aware of and respond to the daily hurts of others, we should be particularly sensitive to notice when people may have an acute need for comfort. When people are physically ill, under stress, unemployed, when they've lost a loved one in death or experienced the trauma of a divorce or separation, when a tragedy has occurred, or when someone's comfort zone is challenged or violated (a job change, move to another city), they will have an enhanced need for comfort.

2. **When you know that someone is hurting, if possible, enter her physical world.**

    When ministering to someone who is hurting, it's best to be with her physically. While it is possible to comfort someone over the phone or in a letter, comfort is best administered in person. It's also more effective to enter into *her* world. If your friend is hurting, instead of saying, "Susan, it sounds like we need to talk. Can you drop by my office this afternoon?" it would be much more effective to say, "Susan, it sounds like we need to talk. Can I come by your office this afternoon? If that's not a good place to talk, we can go somewhere to get a cup of coffee."

3. **Enter her emotional world.**

    We all live in several "worlds" at one time. Physically, we are always somewhere; mentally, we're wherever our thoughts take us; and we also have an emotional world in which we live. At any given moment it's easy to assess where someone is physically (for instance, "in this room, sitting on the couch"), but it's more difficult to determine where she is emotionally. Ministering comfort to someone involves entering into her emotional world by actually feeling as she is feeling.

    One day I was meeting with a group of ministers for a time of fellowship and sharing. Sitting in a circle, we began to share our current struggles. One pastor vulnerably related how he had just been fired from his church. As he was telling his story, another pastor began to gently weep. He was so entering into the pain of this fellow pastor (whom he didn't even know) that he cried for him. He identified so closely with the man's sorrow and so entered into his emotional world that he became heavy in heart himself. The hurting pastor, when he realized that this man was weeping for him, was deeply touched. It made a profound impact on him.

    > The hurting pastor, when he realized that this man was weeping for him, was deeply touched. It made a profound impact on him.

4. **Listen.**

    A good comforter must be a good listener. The one who has been hurt should do most of the talking, and the person comforting should simply listen. While comforting someone, if we talk too much, we will inevitably move out of the realm of comfort. So when comforting, listen a lot and let your words be few.

    When listening, try to discern how the hurting person is *feeling*. She may spend most of the time sharing facts and details about a particular incident, but as she shares, try to discern the painful emotions she must be feeling.

5. **When someone needs comfort, avoid these unproductive responses:**

- Advice/instruction—"Let me give you some steps of action to solve the problem." "Maybe next time that happens you should … "
- Logic/reasoning—"Let me analyze the situation and tell you why it happened." "I think the reason that happened was because … "
- Pep talk—"You're a winner! You'll make it through these tough times!" "I'm sure tomorrow will be a better day."
- Minimize—"Sure it hurts, but get it in perspective; there's a lot going on that's good." "Aren't you being overly sensitive?"
- Anger—"That makes me so mad! They shouldn't get away with that!" "I'm so upset that you keep getting yourself hurt."
- Martyr's complex—"I had something similar happen to me." "After the kind of day I had, let me tell you what hurt really feels like."
- Personal fear/anxiety—"I'm afraid that's going to affect my life too."
- Mr. "Fix it"—"I can't believe that salesman talked to you like that. I'm calling the store right now and talking to his boss." "I know you must have been scared when you had a flat tire on that lonely road. Tomorrow I'll take the car in and get a whole new set of tires."
- Silence/neglect—"_____".
- Spiritualizing—"Well, you know that God will work all of this out for your good." "Remember what the Bible says that Joseph said when his brothers mistreated him, 'They meant it for evil but God meant it for good.'" "It's good to know that we are more than conquerors through Christ!"

Which of these nine unproductive responses are you most likely to engage in? Why?

_____

6. **Learn the "vocabulary" of comfort.**

Many people simply don't know what to say to someone who needs to be comforted. We have never developed an appropriate vocabulary. Here are some phrases that can be spoken to a hurting person:

- "I'm so sorry that you are hurting. I hurt for you."
- "It saddens me that you are hurting. I am sad that you are sad because I love you and care for you."
- "I'm on your side and I'm committed to help you through this difficult time."
- "It saddens me that you felt _____ [embarrassed, rejected, belittled]. I know that must have hurt."
- "I know that you're hurting. I just had to come be with you."

When speaking words of comfort, it's also important that our tone of voice be complimentary to what is being said. Our speech should be warm, sincere and gentle.

7. **In addition to verbal expressions of empathy, use appropriate physical touch to minister comfort.**

If done sensitively and sincerely, a warm embrace, holding hands, or wiping a fevered brow can bring comfort.

8. **Express your sadness non-verbally.**

Tears shed for someone else can convey love beyond words.

When was the last time you cried for someone else? _____

9. **If appropriate, minister to the source of the person's pain.**

When someone we care for is hurting, a natural tendency is to want to fix what went wrong. But the first and most important thing to do is to minister to the person who is hurting. Then, perhaps at a later time and in a different setting, address the cause of the pain. For instance:

- Your eight-year-old daughter is crying because the teacher embarrassed her in front of her classmates. What dad wouldn't want to "fix" that situation: "Sweetheart, that makes me so mad. I'm going to school with you tomorrow, meet with your teacher and the principal, and get this straightened out."

- Your co-worker has been taken advantage of by a fellow employee. Your typical response might be, "Let me deal with this. I'm meeting with the boss this afternoon. I'll let him know what happened, and he and I will straighten this out."

- Your friend just found out that she has cancer. You might be tempted to say, "I know the best cancer doctor in town. First thing in the morning, I'll call her and get you an appointment."

There's basically nothing wrong with wanting to fix a situation that has caused or is causing hurt to someone you care about. But don't confuse fixing the situation with comforting the individual. The first priority is to comfort the hurt.

And it's best not to mix the two together ("I'm so sorry this happened to you; just wait till I get hold of … "). Don't even place them too close to one another ("It hurts me that you feel taken advantage of." [fifteen seconds later] "Give me the telephone number of the mechanic that worked on your car; I'll get this issue settled in a hurry.") That's why it may be best to "fix" the problem at a different setting. During the initial contact, concentrate on comforting; at a subsequent setting, address how the issue causing the hurt can be resolved.

I began my ministry in 1971 so I've had several decades of ministry experience. I am sad to say that it wasn't until around 1996 that I began to understand how to comfort someone. It's amazing, that I could be a minister of the gospel for 25 years and not know how to perform one of the most basic of ministries, but unfortunately, that was the case.

I remember feeling so awkward when trying to minister to someone who was hurting. I didn't know what to say so I would inevitably say something I shouldn't have (like one of the unproductive responses listed on page 78). Finally, I learned the simple principles of how to comfort someone.

I share this in order to place the following anecdote into proper perspective. This story is about how I did it right, but for every story I could tell about how I properly comforted someone, I could tell fifty about how I messed up.

When Lauren, my oldest daughter, was a junior in high school we moved to the Dallas area. We enrolled Lauren in a private school for her junior year but it turned out to be academically lacking so for her senior year we transferred her to another private academy. Three schools in three years. That's tough.

Fortunately, her final year went well. The school was a great experience for her. The next year she started college at the University of North Texas, just 30 miles north of Dallas.

One day she announced that on the weekend she was going to her alma mater's homecoming. I immediately had some red flags go up in my spirit.

That Friday night she was dressed up in a starched Oxford shirt and starched blue jeans. You know it's going to be a big event when someone starches her blue jeans. I waited up for Lauren that evening, not just concerned for her physical safety, but more for her emotional well being. I realized that she had only attended the school for one year whereas most of the students had been friends for many years; some had been together for all twelve years. I was afraid the evening might not meet all of her expectations.

When she came home that evening, as soon as she walked through the door I could tell by her countenance that she had been hurt.

When I asked her what had happened, she sadly replied, "Daddy, I was so excited to go to the game and see all my friends. But when I got there, it was as if I was a ghost. I would go up to one group and try to engage in conversation but would be "nicely snubbed." I tried another group of friends but the same thing happened. Finally, I sat by myself up in the grandstands. After the game I just came home."

I had one hurting daughter.

I was tempted to respond with all ten of the unproductive responses listed earlier in this chapter:

- Advice/instruction – "Lauren, the next time that happens, be more assertive. Get in peoples' faces and demand that they talk to you."
- Logic/reasoning – "Lauren, the reason that happened is because most of your school mates had know each other for years. You were only at the school for one year."
- Pep talk – "Lauren, you're a winner. You have a new life at the University. Tomorrow will be another day. Think positively!"
- Minimize – "Lauren, don't you think you're making too big a deal about this situation. It's only one small incident on the radar screen of your life."
- Anger – "I'm so mad at your classmates. We had them all over to the house for a graduation party. They shouldn't have treated you like that."
- Martyr's complex – "Talk about hurt, let me tell you about what happened to me when I was a freshman in college … "
- Mr. "Fix-it" – "Just wait until next Monday. I'll call that school and complain. They ought to do a better job of taking care of their alumni."
- Silence/neglect – "Lauren, let's go to bed."
- Spiritualizing – "Well Lauren, remember that all things work together for them that love God. And I know you love God, so this will all work out all right."

But fortunately, I resisted all unproductive responses and just administered comfort. We went into the den, sat on the couch and I asked Lauren to share with me how she was feeling. I then uttered those choice words that minister life and health to a hurting soul – words of comfort. "Lauren, I'm so sorry that happened. I know you must have felt embarrassed and neglected. I hurt for you because I love you. You are very dear to me. I'm so sorry you are hurting."

Lauren cried, I held her, we talked for a few minutes, and then she got up and went to bed – the hurt was gone.

While the memory of that evening will no doubt linger in her mind (we really cannot forget painful events), I'm convinced that the emotional pain is gone.

When we comfort someone who is mourning we will experience a miracle. It is the miracle of Matthew 5:4, "Blessed are those who mourn for they shall be comforted." If you rearrange the order of the verbs in this verse we get: mourning + comforting = being blessed. It is a miracle. How can someone go from feeling sad to feeling blessed? Through the ministry of comfort. My daughter entered the house that evening feeling sad, she went to bed thirty minutes later feeling blessed. How? Someone she loved ministered the One Another of Comfort to her just when she needed it.

Mom's Investment

Several weeks before I started first grade, I broke my ankle. I was playing on a merry-go-round at the city park and got my leg caught between two pieces of metal. The metal didn't give; my ankle joint did. Dad came to my rescue, picked me up, and took me to the house. He couldn't tell by looking whether or not my ankle was broken, so he assumed it was just sprained. The next day, X-rays would reveal that it was indeed broken. I had to endure the night with a broken ankle. At the time, my mother was working at a grocery store and got off work late at night. I'll never forget that evening when she came home and saw me in pain. As soon as she walked in my room and saw me lying on the bed crying, she started crying. Before she even said a word, I sensed her love and empathy through her tears. The first words out of her mouth were not, "How did this happen?" or "Dad, why didn't you take him to the hospital?" but rather, "Oh, sweetheart, I'm so sorry, I'm so sorry."—phrases of comfort that ministered to a hurting child. My mother comforted me. Thanks, Mom.

Write your own definition of Comfort One Another.

_____

_____

_____

Personal Journal

1. Write about a time when someone truly comforted you.

   _____

   _____

2. Write about a time when you needed comfort but instead, someone responded inappropriately (see page 78 for a list of unproductive responses).

   _____

   _____

3. Write about a time when you should have comforted someone but instead, you responded with one of the unproductive responses (see page 78).

   _____

   _____

4. Write about a time when you truly comforted someone else.

   _____

   _____

5. How might your two secret recipients need the ministry of comfort in their lives?

   Secret Recipient _____

   Unchurched recipient _____

6. On a scale from 1 to 10 (1 being, "I need to greatly improve" and 10 being, "I do a good job"), how well do you do at comforting others? Ask your OA Partner to rate you.

   I rated myself a _____.
   My OA partner rated me a _____.

Practical Suggestion #5

Learn to sense which One Another a person may need at any given time.

Ephesians 4:29 says, "Do not let any unwholesome talk come out of your mouths, but only what is helpful for building others up *according to their needs*, that it may benefit those who listen" (emphasis added). According to this verse, unwholesome words are not just curse words or words that denigrate someone such as slander or rumors; unwholesome words are also words that don't meet the need of the moment. For instance, if someone needs to be comforted, words of instruction ("Next time that happens, do this ... ") will be perceived as unwholesome. If someone needs your involvement and support, mere words of encouragement ("I'll be praying for you ... ") will be of little benefit.

We need to determine what people *need*, not just what *we* want to *give*.

When you finish this book, you should have a good understanding of eight of the One Anothers (there are individual chapters on eight of them) and at least a working knowledge of another eight (the last chapter contains several paragraphs on eight additional One Anothers). Consider each of the One Anothers to be a type of emotional/spiritual medicine that can be dispensed to needy people. Consider yourself a doctor of sorts, able to prescribe just the right medicine for any particular illness. If a patient suffers from diabetes, a physician wouldn't prescribe medicine for high blood pressure. Likewise, if your friend needs acceptance, don't administer a generous dose of admonition and think you've done him a favor.

We need to match a particular One Another to every "need of the moment." If we do, we will "benefit" those to whom we minister. If we're not careful to match the gift with the need, we may actually cause damage. Can you imagine the emotional fallout of admonishing someone who actually needs acceptance?

How can we learn to sense people's needs? *Listen* to what they say, *observe* their body language, *discover* what they're going through, *ask* questions about their lives, *and be sensitive* to the Holy Spirit's leadership. It's really not that hard.

Learn to ask non-intimidating questions such as, "What's been going on in your life?" "How are you feeling?"

These questions provide an opportunity for people to share at whatever level of vulnerability they are comfortable with.

A little boy said to his father, "Let's play darts. I'll throw, and you say 'Wonderful!'" That young boy obviously needed some approval.

After more than forty years of marriage, a woman's husband suddenly died. For several months after the funeral, she sat alone in her house with the shades drawn. Finally she decided she needed to do something about her situation. The loneliness was killing her.

She remembered that her husband had a friend who owned a nice pet store—a pet might be good company. So she dropped in one afternoon and told the storeowner she wanted a pet that could be a real companion. He led her to one of his prized parrots.

"Does it talk?"

"Absolutely—a real chatterbox. Everybody who comes in the store is astounded by this parrot's friendly disposition and wide vocabulary."

"Sold!" She bought the parrot and hauled it home in a large cage. At last she had a companion she could talk to, one who could answer back. Perfect!

But there was a problem. A full week passed without the bird's saying one word. Beginning to worry, she dropped by the pet shop.

"How's the parrot doing? Quite a talker, huh?"

"Not one word. I haven't been able to get a sound out of the bird. I'm worried."

"Well, did you buy a *mirror* when you got the bird last week?"

"Mirror? No. There's no mirror in the cage."

"That's your problem. A parrot needs a mirror. It's funny, but while looking at itself, a parrot starts to feel comfortable." So she bought the mirror and put it into the cage.

Time passed, still nothing. Each day the woman talked to the bird, but not a peep came out of its beak. Another week passed without a word.

"The parrot isn't talking," she told the pet storeowner. "I'm worried. All that money, the mirror—and still nothing."

"Say, did you buy a *ladder* when you got the cage?"

"A ladder? No. Will that make it talk?"

"Works like a charm. The parrot will look in the mirror and get a little exercise, climbing up and down this ladder several times. Before long you won't believe what you hear."

She bought the ladder and put it into the cage next to the mirror ... and waited. And waited. Eight days later, still nothing. She returned to the store in tears with the same complaint.

"Did you buy a *swing*?"

"A swing! No. I have a cage, a mirror, and a ladder. I had no idea I needed a swing."

"You gotta have a swing. A parrot needs to feel completely at home. It glances in the mirror, takes a stroll up and down the ladder, and before long it's on the swing enjoying itself—and bingo! I've found that parrots usually talk when they are perched on a swing."

The woman bought the swing. She attached it to the top of the cage near the ladder. Ten days passed ... still, absolute silence.

Suddenly she came bursting into the pet store, really steaming. The owner met her at the counter.

"Hey, how's my parrot? I'll bet . . ."

"It died! My expensive bird is dead in the bottom of the cage."

"Well, I can't believe that. I'm just shocked. Did it ever say anything at all?"

"Yes, as a matter of fact, it did. As it lay there taking its last few breaths, it said very faintly, 'Don't they have any *food* down at that store?'"[2]

We must be sensitive to perceive what people really need at any given moment and be prepared to meet that need.

Learning to Match the Proper One Another with the Presenting Need

Fill in the blanks with the appropriate One Another:

1. When I sense that someone is overwhelmed, I need to _____ him.

2. When I see someone that I've never met before, I need to take the initiative to _____ her.

3. When I come home from school or work, I need to _____ each person in my house.

4. When I meet someone who is different from me (race, color, theological persuasion), I need to make a conscientious effort to _____ him.

5. When I and another person have different preferences, I need to _____ him.

6. When I sense that someone is discouraged, I need to _____ him.

7. When I sense that someone is becoming "weary in well doing," I need to _____ her.

8. When someone is violating Scripture, I need to _____ him.

9. When someone has offended me, I need to _____ him.

10. When I have offended someone, I need to _____ to him.

11. When someone is hurting, I need to _____ him.

12. When someone is embarrassed or feels rejected, I need to _____ her.

Which One Another might the following people need right now in their lives?

<u>Person</u>   <u>The One Another they need</u>

Secret recipient _____   _____

Unchurched recipient _____   _____

OA Partner _____   _____

Family member _____   _____

Powerful Result #5

The One Anothers bring glory to God.

I have been a worship leader for thirty years, and I have written three books on worship. But until recently, I never noticed the last phrase of Romans 15:7, which has drastically impacted my concept of worship. Romans 15:7 says, "Accept one another, then, just as Christ accepted you, *in order to bring praise to God*" (emphasis added). Accepting others is an effective means of praise and worship. There's no mention of music or phrases of adoration—none of the functions we normally associate with worship. Just accepting others.

Can you imagine beginning a Sunday morning worship service with this announcement: "Friends, we have gathered today to worship the living God. This morning we're going to engage in biblical worship. There will be no singing or playing of instruments. Instead, spend the next thirty minutes getting to know the person who is sitting next to you, and as you do, reassure him that you accept him just the way he is."

It would, no doubt, be a unique service, but according to Romans 15:7, God would accept it as pleasing worship.

But does this principle apply only to accepting others? My theory is that the same holds true for all of the One Anothers. I believe that when we engage in any of the various ministries—comfort, encourage, prefer, admonish—God is praised. The following verses seem to substantiate the theory:

- "Through Jesus, therefore, let us continually offer to God a sacrifice of praise—the fruit of lips that confess his name. And do not forget to do good and to share with others, for with such sacrifices God is pleased" (Hebrews 13:15–16). Two sacrifices are mentioned: our talk (fruit of our lips) and what we do (good deeds and sharing with others).

- "You will be made rich in every way so that you can be generous on every occasion, and through us your generosity will result in thanksgiving to God. This service that you perform is not only supplying the needs of God's people but is also overflowing in many expressions of thanks to God. Because of the service by which you have proved yourselves, men will praise God for the obedience that accompanies your confession of the gospel of Christ, and for your generosity in sharing with them and with everyone else" (2 Corinthians 9:11–13). God sees the "service that supplies the needs of God's people" as expressions of thanks.

Why do the One Anothers bring glory to God? I can think of several reasons.

1. **When we minister to one another, we are ministering to the body of Christ, and when we minister to the body of Christ, we are ministering to Christ himself (see Matthew 25:34–40).**

In a strange but sure way, when we comfort one another, we are comforting Christ, and when we accept one another, we are accepting Christ.

Prior to his conversion, the apostle Paul persecuted the followers of Christ. When Jesus confronted Paul on the road to Damascus, he said, "Saul, Saul, why do you persecute *me*?" (Acts 9:4; emphasis added). When believers are persecuted, Jesus feels persecuted. In like manner, when we minister grace to believers, Jesus feels blessed.

2. The One Anothers bring joy to the heart of God.

Have you ever wondered, "What makes God happy? What delights his heart?" There are, no doubt, many answers; here are two possibilities.

God is blessed when his children obediently carry out his divine plan. In Luke 10, Jesus appointed seventy-two disciples and sent them out two by two. After obeying his instructions and fulfilling their mission, the disciples returned "with joy" (v. 17) and reported that everything went according to plans. When Jesus heard their good report, he too was filled with joy (v. 21) and rejoiced with the Father: "I praise you, Father, Lord of heaven and earth, because you have hidden these things from the wise and learned, and revealed them to little children. Yes, Father, for this was your good pleasure" (v. 21). In essence Jesus exclaimed, "Yes! Your plan is working! The divine strategy has just been alpha tested and found to be fully viable! And the disciples whom I have been training—they've got it! They obeyed and found personal joy in doing so!"

God is blessed as he observes us fulfilling his plan. Relative to our study of the One Anothers, God is blessed when we obey all 35 directives.

Another thing that delights God's heart can be found in the following text. Read it carefully. "As the Father has loved me, so have I loved you. Now remain in my love. If you obey my commands, you will remain in my love, just as I have obeyed my Father's commands and remain in his love. I have told you this so that my joy may be in you and that your joy may be complete" (John 15:9–11). Notice the word *joy*. Sharing the love of Christ brings joy to his heart and to ours.

3. When we effectively minister the One Anothers, people will inevitably be drawn to the source of so great a love.

I once heard the term *star witness* defined in this way: "We Christians often witness to others by initiating a conversation in which we explain the claims of Christ. A star witness is a believer who so lives the life of Christ that people approach her and comment, 'There's something different about you. How is it that you're able to love people so thoroughly? I want what you have!'"

When people are attracted to our acts of love, we can then introduce them to the source of our love. We can honestly say, "It's not my love I'm giving; it's God's." They will be drawn to him, and he will be glorified.

Group Time—Session Six

Each member of the group should give his or her individual response to the first four questions. Allow about two minutes for each person's response. Allow all group members to share their answer to question #1 before proceeding to question #2.

1. What was the most interesting concept in this chapter?

2. Referring back to last week's lesson, share about a time this week when you were able to encourage someone else and a time when you should have encouraged someone else but did not.

3. Share your responses to the first three Personal Journal entries in this chapter (page 82).

4. Review the unproductive responses to a hurting person that are listed under #5 of the "Practical Ways to Comfort One Another" (p. 78). Which are you most tempted to offer?

As a group, process these discussion questions:

a. How will comforting other people be a testimony to "all men" (John 13:34) that we belong to the Lord and that we are his disciples?

b. Depending on the level of trust that your group has developed, you may want to minister to each other's hurts in the following way: Each member of the group share a hurt from your childhood and allow the members of the group to comfort you.

c. On a scale from 1 to 10 (1 being, "We're not too good at this" and 10 being, "We're really good at this"), how good is your church/organization at comforting people?

Homework:
Read and process chapter 7.

CARRY ONE ANOTHER'S BURDENS

"Carry each other's burdens, and in this way you will fulfill the law of Christ" (Galatians 6:2).

A ndrew Davison tells of a life-changing lesson he learned from the great humanitarian, theologian, and physician, Albert Schweitzer.

Dr. Schweitzer was eighty-five years old when I visited his jungle hospital at Lambarene, on the banks of the Ogowe River. One morning, the equatorial sun was beating down mercilessly, and we were walking up a hill with Dr. Schweitzer. Suddenly he left us and strode across the slope of the hill to a place where an African woman was struggling upward with a huge armload of wood for the cook fires. I watched with both admiration and concern as the eighty-five-year-old man took the entire load of wood and carried it on up the hill for the relieved woman. When we all reached the top of the hill, one of the members of our group asked Dr. Schweitzer why he did things like that, implying that in that heat and at his age he should not. Albert Schweitzer, looking right at all of us and pointing to the woman, said simply, "No one should ever have to carry a burden like that alone."[1]

Different Types of Burdens

Throughout our lives, we will inevitably encounter challenges that are too big for one person to handle. When we do, we need someone to support us; we need someone to help carry our burden. The burden may be:

> Physical—"I need help moving the furniture in my apartment."
> Mental—"I need help completing my project at work."
> Emotional—"I can't seem to get over the loss of my mother."
> Spiritual—"I have some questions about my faith."

But they all have one thing in common—we can't bear the burden alone; we need someone to help.

Different Sizes of Burdens

In Galatians 6, the apostle Paul talks about the burdens we all inevitably face. He seems to contradict himself because in verse 2 he says to "carry each other's burdens" and then three verses later he says "each one should carry his own burden." There appears to be a conflict in what he's saying until we learn that he uses two different Greek words for our English word *burden*. The word used in verse 5 (*phortion*) refers to a small load like a light backpack. But in verse 2, the Greek word for burden is *baros,* which describes an overwhelming load, a burden so heavy that it is crushing the back of the person who is trying to bear it.

Indeed, all of us have our peculiar, personal struggles in life that we may need to bear ourselves (although we'll probably need generous doses of encouragement). But often our burden is too large for one person to bear; we need someone to help bear our burden.

What are some of the smaller, "backpack"-size challenges that you face?

_____

_____

What are some of the overwhelming loads with which you struggle?

_____

_____

Encouragement and Burden Bearing—Contrasted and Compared

While there are many similarities between "Encourage One Another" and "Carry One Another's Burdens" (they both involve giving aid to someone), there is often a significant difference. Encouragement usually only requires an emotional involvement on our part, but burden bearing often requires that we become physically involved. Burden bearing is participatory. For instance, if I'm discouraged about a relationship, I may need you to simply pray with me or write me a note of encouragement. But if my task is to move a grand piano, I need more than your prayers and notes of encouragement—I need you to roll up your sleeves and help carry the weight. Indeed, when we need support but only receive encouragement, the encouragement may seem inadequate—if not downright offensive.

The story is told of a rabbit being chased by a dog. The onlookers were telling the rabbit to run hard and escape. "Thank you for your kind encouragement," said the rabbit, "but for goodness sake shoot the dog."

Indeed, when we need support but only **receive encouragement,** the encouragement may seem inadequate—*if not downright offensive.*

Although bearing burdens often requires our physical involvement, it may also demand our emotional involvement. For instance, if a single parent is having difficulty with raising a child, we will want to help bear the emotional burden of the situation, in addition to helping in physical ways.

Linda Mango tells this story about a father who was willing to share in the emotional trauma of his young son:

> While working at a medical center, I noticed a distinguished gentleman and his young son on their daily visits to the chemotherapy center. An impeccably tailored suit and a head of lush salt-and-pepper hair made the man stand out. As I admired him and his smiling five-year-old, I found it impossible to tell who was receiving treatment.
>
> One day, as they walked past, my attention was drawn to the boy. The cap he usually wore was missing, and I could now see a shiny bald head. I turned toward the father. To my surprise, he was as bald as his son.
>
> "Look at my dad!" the boy said cheerfully. "He shaved his head so we'd look the same. We're going to grow our hair back together!"
>
> His father simply smiled, looking more distinguished than ever.[2]

What are some emotional issues that you deal with that are too big for you to handle alone?

_____

_____

Burden bearing may require making a significant commitment. It says, "I don't want you to bear your burden alone; as long as the burden is yours, the burden is also mine." This commitment may last for years and require a significant investment of time, resources, and energy.

In Booker T. Washington's autobiography, *Up From Slavery*, Mr. Washington recalled a beautiful incident of an older brother's love. He said the shirts worn on his plantation by the slaves were made of a rough, bristly, inexpensive flax fiber. As a young boy, the garment was so abrasive to his tender, sensitive skin that it caused him a great deal of pain and discomfort. His older brother, moved by his brother's suffering, would wear Booker's new shirts until they were broken in and smoother to the touch. Booker said it was one of the most striking acts of kindness he had experienced among his fellow slaves.

When someone is carrying a heavy burden, he is particularly susceptible to being taken advantage of and manipulated. This vulnerability and exposure is minimized as we lovingly come alongside him and help bear his burden.

Practical Ways to Bear One Another's Burdens

1. **Anticipate times in people's lives when they might need help, and be available to help during those times**. People are particularly blessed when we anticipate their needs and take the initiative to help, instead of us waiting until they are overwhelmed and pleading for help.

2. **Because bearing other people's burdens often requires a major commitment of time, allocate some time in your weekly schedule for this ministry.**

"This month, I'm going to devote every Saturday morning to helping my daughter with her science fair project."

"I'm going to reserve several hours a week to help a friend with his new business."

"This summer, I'm going to take two weeks of vacation to help build a new sanctuary for a church in Honduras."

"My neighbors just had twins. Every Thursday evening I'm going to volunteer to baby-sit their children so they can have some time together."

3. **When necessary, be willing to perform menial, physical tasks.** Oftentimes, bearing other people's burdens involves getting physically involved and often this means performing tedious, boring and "unskilled" labor. Even though you are a "professional," in order to bear someone's burden you may need to wash dishes, trim bushes, change diapers, type a report, or deliver a package. Sometimes the tendency may be to say "I'll just pay to have it done; my time is more valuable than that." But it may be that the person you're helping needs more than just getting the job done —he needs your personal involvement.

4. **Help facilitate group efforts which bear people's burdens.** Learn to recognize and respond to opportunities in which a group of people can and should respond to a pressing need.

- When a family experiences an extended sickness, coordinate people who can take meals to the family.

- When a single person needs to move to another residence, coordinate a moving party.

Gordon McDonald tells a compelling story about a woman who was willing to bear the burdens of another.

[My wife] Gail and I were in an airplane, seated almost at the back. As the plane loaded up, a woman with two small children came down the aisle to take the seat right in front of us. And behind her, came another woman. The two women took the A and C seats, one of the children sat in the middle seat, and the second child sat on the lap of one of the women, I figured these were two mothers traveling together with their kids, and I hoped the kids wouldn't be noisy.

The flight started, and my prayer wasn't answered. The air was turbulent, the children cried a lot—their ears hurt—and it was a miserable flight. I watched as these two women kept trying to comfort these children. The woman at the window played with the child in the middle seat, trying to make her feel good and paying lots of attention to her.

I thought, *Boy these women get a medal for what they are doing.* But everything went downhill from there. Toward the last part of the flight, the child in the middle seat got sick. The next thing I knew she was losing everything from every part of her body. The diaper wasn't on tight, and before long a stench began to rise throughout the cabin. It was unbearable!

I could see over the top of the seat that stuff you don't want me to describe was all over everything. It was on this woman's clothes. It was all over the seat. It was on the floor. It was one of the most repugnant things I had seen in a long time.

The woman next to the window patiently comforted the child and tried her best to clean up the mess and make something good out of a bad situation. The plane landed, and when we pulled up to the gate all of us were ready to exit that plane as fast as we could. The flight attendant came up with paper towels, handed them to the woman in the window seat, and said, "Here ma'am, these are for your little girl."

The woman said, "This isn't my little girl."

"Aren't you traveling together?"

"No, I've never met this woman and these children before in my life."

Suddenly, I realized I had just seen mercy lived out. A lot of us would have just died in this circumstance. This woman found the opportunity to give mercy. She was, in the words of Christ, "the person who was the neighbor." [4]

Mom's Investment

 ■ Back in the late '60s, dune buggies were a popular craze. These eye-catching, off-road, customized vehicles promised hours of fun-filled transportation. While some people simply purchased the cars from a conversion shop, I was determined to build my own. ■ The process seemed simple enough: Take the body off a Volkswagen Beetle, shorten the chassis 13¾ inches, bolt the fiberglass dune-buggy body onto the chassis, hook up the appropriate cables, and off you go. That might be a simple process for a trained mechanic, but it was quite a challenge for a sixteen-year-old boy. ■ But Mom was there to help. ■ I can remember one particular evening when I was trying to mount the battery up into the battery cage. I was out in the garage, it was about ten o'clock at night, it was freezing, and I was lying on my back underneath the engine trying to shove the battery up into the right spot. I had the wrong size battery, so it was a tight fit. ■ My vivid emotional memory of the evening is looking up through the engine compartment and seeing my mother's face. She was out there in the garage dressed in her robe and slippers handing me wrenches and encouraging me on, "Oh, Don Jr., be careful. Don't let the battery hit you in the face." I'm sure she would have preferred being in her warm bed rather than in the frigid garage, but there she was, carrying my burden. ■ I also remember a time when I needed to buy a part for the dune buggy, but I had run out of personal money. Even though money was always extremely tight around our house, Mom wrote a check for the part. I'm sure we had to do without something in the coming days, but whatever it was, Mom didn't think it was more important than supporting my building project. ■ In retrospect, the significance of the dune-buggy project was more than just about cool transportation; it was a character-building project. It was about creative energy; it was about initiative; it was about dreams. One of my strengths as an adult is my ability to start with a blank sheet of paper and create something from scratch—to dream, initiate and create. Mom's willingness to help "carry my burden" on that project—handing me the right wrench or buying a part— helped prepare me for more serious, far-reaching projects. ■ Thanks, Mom.

Write your own definition of Carry One Another's Burdens.

_____

_____

_____

Personal Journal

1. Write about a time in your life when someone helped carry your burden.

   _____

   _____

2. When was the last time you helped carry someone's burden? Write about your experience.

   _____

   _____

3. When was the last time you *should* have helped carry someone's burden but didn't?

   _____

   _____

4. In Psalm 68:19, the psalmist said, "Praise be to the Lord, to God our Savior, who daily bears our burdens." What burdens are you currently having to bear which you have not cast upon the Lord? Read 1 Peter 5:7 and then, based on this promise, share your burdens with God and allow him to carry them.

5. What can you do this week to help bear the burdens of your two secret recipients?

   Secret recipient _____

   Unchurched recipient _____

6. List your closest family members and friends and write down ways in which they may need you to help bear their burdens.

   Name _____ Burden to bear _____

   Name _____ Burden to bear _____

   Name _____ Burden to bear _____

   Name _____ Burden to bear _____

7. On a scale from 1 to 10 (1 being, "I need to greatly improve" and 10 being, "I do a good job"), how well do you do at carrying other people's burdens? Ask your OA Partner to rate you.

   I rated myself a _____.

   My OA partner rated me a _____.

Practical Suggestion #6
Be diligent to minister all thirty-five of the One Anothers.

Because every person is different (unique personality, spiritual gift, family heritage, etc.) we each have certain One Anothers that come naturally (ones that are easy to "perform") and those that we struggle to engage in. For instance, a person with the gift of prophecy may find it easy and natural to Admonish One Another but struggle with Comfort One Another. Likewise, it may be more difficult for a shy person to Greet One Another than it will be for someone who is an extrovert.

But regardless of our natural inclinations, we need to minister all of the One Anothers. We should never have the attitude: "I'm just not an out-going person so I'm not going to greet others." Or, "I'm a very decisive individual so I am disinclined to prefer others."

For instance, I am a quiet, reserved person. When I go out to eat with friends, I am perfectly content to sit back and let others carry the conversation. I'm never the life of the party, and that's fine with me. That's just the way I am. But I can't use this as an excuse to be unfriendly.

My wife has the gift of prophecy; she usually has a "black-or-white" approach to life. She is an incredibly insightful person who doesn't mind speaking her mind. Because of her personality and her gift, being empathetic and comforting doesn't come naturally. She's not the person to go to when you're hurting. But she has come to realize that just because this is her natural bent, she is not exempt from the command to Comfort One Another. She may have to work at it more than someone who has the gift of mercy, but she is,

nevertheless, obliged to comfort hurting people.

So, as you're studying the various One Anothers, don't pick and choose which ones you're going to do. Yes, you'll be naturally inclined toward some more than others, but be diligent to minister all of them.

Consider the following One Anothers and put a check [✓] next to the ones that you are naturally inclined to perform. Put an [x] next to the ones that don't come naturally.

Comfort	Greet
Prefer	Accept
Admonish	Honor
Encourage	Be devoted to
Wait for	Rejoice with
Pray for	Be Kind to
Serve	Confess Your Faults
Forgive	Offer Hospitality to

Once we have a practical knowledge of the One Anothers, we are responsible to minister them; if we don't, we have sinned. "Anyone, then, who knows the good he ought to do and doesn't do it, sins" (James 4:17). This verse speaks of the sins of omission as opposed to the sins of commission. We need to realize that sin is not just doing that which is wrong but also *not* doing that which is right. John spoke of this in 1 John 3:17, "If anyone has material possessions and sees his brother in need but has no pity on him, how can the love of God be in him?" Once we become aware of the One Anothers, we are responsible for dispensing *all* of them. To be indifferent or apathetic is sin.

Powerful Result #6

The One Anothers are an effective tool for evangelism. As we minister them, people will be drawn to Jesus.

The last phrase of the 11th Commandment reads, "All men will know that you are my disciples if you love one another" (John 13:34). The One Anothers are the distinguishing marks of a Christian. Jesus does not say, "All men will know that you are my disciples if you memorize more Scriptures than they do" or " if you live a pious, puritanical life." But rather, all men (unbelievers as well as believers) will know that we belong to Christ when we demonstrate love.

A family in our church comes from a Catholic background. Their testimony is very telling. Years ago, a member of their family, a young lady, was attending a small college where she was responsible for leading a Catholic Bible study on the campus. A Protestant Bible study, led by another female student, met at the same time. The two student leaders lived in the same dorm and became friends. There was some rivalry between the two groups because they were contending for the same students. For the most part, the competition between the two Bible studies was friendly, but at times it was diplomatically tense.

During spring break, the leader of the Protestant group traveled to Italy and, while in Rome, visited the Vatican. In the gift shop, she bought some prayer beads for her friend.

When classes resumed, she presented the prayer beads to her friend as a gift, saying, "When I was in Rome, I was thinking about you." Stunned at such an act of kindness and deference, the Catholic girl commented, "I thought you didn't believe in prayer beads!" "I don't," replied her friend, "but I know that you do. I bought them for you because I love you." To which the Catholic girl responded, "My religion does not allow me to do that. I want what you have."

The simple acts of Prefer One Another, Accept One Another, and Be Kind to One Another had such a dramatic impact on the girl's life that she accepted Christ as her Savior, shared the good news with her family, and thirty members of her immediate family came to know Christ, including my friend and his wife.

Indeed, the One Anothers are a powerful evangelistic tool. As we share with people God's unconditional love, they will be drawn to the source of so great a love.

One Sunday on their way home from church, a little girl turned to her mother and said, "Mommy, the preacher's sermon this morning confused me." The mother said, "Oh? Why is that?" The little girl replied, "He said that God is bigger than we are." "Yes, that's true honey." "And he also said that God lives in us? Is that true Mommy?" Again the mother replied, "Yes." "Well," said the little girl, "if God is bigger than us and he lives in us, wouldn't he show through?"

He should show through, and people should see his unceasing love expressed through us.

The 11th Commandment is, perhaps, the key to the continuation of Christ's ministry on earth. In the verse that precedes the 11th Commandment, Jesus speaks of his impending departure: "My children, I will be with you only a little while longer. You will look for me, and just as I told the Jews, so I tell you now: Where I am going, you cannot come" (John 13:33). The entire chapter is Jesus' final instructions to his disciples, his departing strategy for kingdom business and the 11th Commandment is set as the foundational principle.

Notice that he doesn't say, "I'm leaving—build lots of buildings" or "I'm leaving—preserve theological orthodoxy" or "I'm leaving—maintain a proper hierarchy among my followers." No, he simply says, "Love one another." It is a simple yet sufficient strategy.

In the February 1977 issue of *Eternity* magazine, Olga Wetzel shares the following story:

The Greyhound bus slowed—then stopped. It was just a wayside stop with a garage and a small store. A young Indian stepped aboard and, after he had paid his fare, he sat down behind me.

It was February. We were traveling from Flagstaff, Arizona, to Albuquerque, New Mexico. The night was cold. In the warm bus, the tired youth was soon asleep. But after about twenty minutes he got up and walked to the front of the bus to ask if we were near his destination.

"We passed there a long time ago," the bus driver snapped. Acknowledging he had known the boy was riding beyond his stop, he asked angrily, "Why didn't you get off?"

The quiet passenger's shoulders drooped. He turned and came back to his seat. Barely had he sat down, when he rose again and went to the driver.

"Will you stop and let me off?" he asked. "I'll walk back."

"No! It's too far and too cold. You'd freeze to death. You'll have to go into Albuquerque and then take a bus back."

Disappointment showed in his walk as he came back to his seat.

"Were you asleep?" I asked him.

"Yes, and my sister was waiting for me there." He dropped into the seat behind me.

I was returning to Wisconsin after serving a quarter term as a volunteer teacher in an Indian mission school. This experience had taught me the hard living conditions of the Indians in the area—the small adobe houses with earth floors, the lack of privacy in those little one-or-two-room houses.

The role played by teenagers was very hard. There was no room for them at home, yet they were not really ready to go out on their own.

All the while we were nearing Albuquerque, a large and strange city. I thought he must be wondering what he would do after he got there. I turned to him and asked, "Are you afraid?"

"Yes," he said, in a "hate-to-admit" way.

"Stay with me," I said, "and I'll help you get on the right bus back."

I asked the driver, "Will you please check with the return driver, so he need not pay return fare?"

"Okay," the driver reluctantly agreed.

"Everything will be all right," I told the boy. "You need not worry about anything." His eyes said, "Thank you!"

We rode on for possibly ten more minutes. Then a hand tapped my shoulder. I turned to see my young friend leaning toward me. In a reverent voice he asked,

"Are you a Christian?"[3]

People should know that we are Christians by our love.

Instead of having to always tell people that we are Christians, wouldn't it be nice to be *recognized as one of his disciples simply by the kind and gracious deeds we do? And wouldn't the truths of the gospel be better received* **by** unbelievers if they first tasted of the goodness of the Lord, being ministered through his body, the church?

Group Time—Session Seven

Each member of the group should give his or her individual response to the first three questions. Allow about two minutes for each person's response. Allow all group members to share their answer to question #1 before proceeding to question #2.

1. What was the most interesting concept in this chapter?

2. Referring back to last week's lesson, share about a time this week when you were able to comfort someone else and a time when you should have comforted someone else but did not.

3. Share your responses to the first three Personal Journal entries in this chapter (page 94).

As a group, process these discussion questions: [These discussion questions have been prioritized. Depending on the time allotted for your group discussion, you may not be able to process all the questions.]

    a. Referring back to the Practical Ways ... #1 (page 91), what are some obvious times when people might need help carrying a burden?

    b. It's been said, "It takes two people to have a child; it takes two people to raise a child." How does this speak to the importance of both the father and mother supporting each other in the raising of children?

    c. In Acts 26:22, Paul said, "I have had God's help to this very day." Have you ever sensed that God was directly bearing your burdens?

    d. In Luke 11:46, Jesus rebuked the religious leaders because they would "not lift one finger to help [people]." Would he have the same response to our lack of helping others?

    e. On a scale from 1 to 10 (1 being, "We need to greatly improve" and 10 being, "We do a good job"), how good is your church/organization at bearing one another's burdens?

Homework:
Read and process chapter 8.

FORGIVE ONE ANOTHER

"Forgiving each other, just as in Christ God forgave you" (Ephesians 4:32).

In her book, *The Liar's Club*, Mary Karr tells the true story of a couple who had a major argument over how much money the wife had spent on sugar. Instead of resolving the simple dispute, both husband and wife held onto their grudge and refused to speak to each other for forty years. Forty years! As if silence wasn't enough to perpetuate their dispute, one day the husband took a saw and literally cut their frame house in half. He nailed up planks over the openings and moved one of the halves to the other side of their acre lot. Husband and wife lived the rest of their lives in separate houses.

Granted, this story is rather extreme, but it does illustrate the damaging effects of unforgiveness. In years of counseling people, I've never known a couple to cut their house in two, or for that matter not to speak to each other for years, but numerous times I've known couples who emotionally cut themselves off from each other because of unresolved offenses. In my home church are two deacons who have not fellowshipped together in years because of an unsettled dispute.

The Divine Nature of Forgiveness

In many ways, forgiving others is the most "divine" of all of the One Anothers. Forgiveness is not of this earth; it is divine in nature. There is nothing in our flesh, in our human nature, that wants to forgive. While there are some One Anothers that are "natural" to human nature (e.g., a mother will have natural, maternal desires to comfort and be devoted to her child), the power to forgive is totally contrary to human nature. We are, perhaps, most Christ-like when we forgive.

The Efficacy of Forgiveness

When we Forgive One Another, it brings freedom in three areas:

1. We (the ones who have been offended) are set free from anger.

When someone wrongs us, we feel hurt. When we are hurt, we become angry. Unresolved anger can escalate into hatred, hatred can lead to bitterness, and bitterness can grow to "cause trouble and defile many" (Hebrews 12:15).

While there are some One Anothers that are "natural" to human nature, the power to forgive is totally contrary to human nature. We are, perhaps, most **Christ-like** when we forgive.

Notice who is most adversely affected by these emotional poisons—we are. Often, our perpetrator is totally unaffected by his sin; he has no guilt nor is he bothered in the least by his sin. At times, he may even be unaware of the offense, or he may be aware but couldn't care less about our hurt. If we refuse to forgive, we suffer twice; we are hurt by the initial offense and hurt again by the residue of unforgiveness. Refusing to forgive is like loading a handgun with the intent to shoot the person who hurt us, but invariably the gun swings around and points at us.

That's why forgiveness is primarily beneficial to the one who has been offended; we do it for ourselves. We may forgive, ostensibly to set a prisoner free, only to discover that the prisoner was us.

Contrary to popular belief, forgiving our offender *does not* release him from guilt. Only his confession can do that. For instance, through Christ's death we have been forgiven, but only as we confess to him our guilt are we set free from the penalty of our sin. The flip side of this is, if we genuinely confess our sin, even though the person we offended refuses to forgive us, we are still released from our guilt.

2. **Relationships can be healed.**

Philip Yancey, in his book *What's So Amazing About Grace*, says, "Forgiveness offers a way out. It does not settle all questions of blame and fairness—often it pointedly evades those questions—but it does allow a relationship to start over, to begin anew."

Forgiveness is life-giving water poured upon a parched, dry relationship. Forgiveness gives us the grace to say, "I'm not sure who is wrong. I'm not even sure what all the issues are. I do know that I love you and want to be at peace with you. I'm sorry for my part in this misunderstanding. Please forgive me; I forgive you."

In the early years of our marriage, my wife and I would fight and argue with each other (perhaps over the price of sugar), and soon the squabble would become so complex that we weren't even sure what the initial issue was. In the heat of the argument, we would drag in issues from the past, present, and even the future! We returned insult for insult. We would dig in our heels, choose our weapons carefully, and engage in mental and emotional battle. But as we have matured and our love has deepened, things have changed. It's not that we never argue anymore, but moments into the battle we become grieved at what's happening and we both Forgive One Another. We usually embrace and say something like, "Sweetheart, I love you. Regardless of what happened to cause this dispute, I want you to know that our relationship is important to me. Please forgive me for my part in this misunderstanding." Is this our way of naively ignoring the issues? No, it's simply our way of establishing and maintaining the transcendence of our relationship.

Write about a current relationship that is strained. How could forgiveness bring healing to this relationship?

_____

_____

_____

The story is told in Spain of a father and his teenage son who had a relationship that had become strained. So the son ran away from home. His father, however, began a journey in search of his rebellious son. Finally, in Madrid, in a last desperate effort to find him, the father put an ad in the newspaper. The ad read: "Dear Paco, Meet me in front of the newspaper office at noon. All is forgiven. I love you. Your father."

The next day at noon in front of the newspaper office, eight hundred "Pacos" showed up. They were all seeking forgiveness and love from their fathers.

Forgiveness is the oil that lubricates strained relationships. Without it, all relationships will spiral downward until they are broken or impaired.[1]

3. Forgiveness offers grace to the offender.

President Lincoln was once asked how he was going to treat the rebellious Southerners when they had finally been defeated and returned to the Union of the United States. The questioner expected that Lincoln would take a dire vengeance, but he answered, "I will treat them as if they had never been away."[2]

When we forgive others, we offer them grace—release from the emotional trauma that sin brings. Forgiving others doesn't necessarily mean that we must pardon them—that is, release them from the legal consequences of their deeds. But when we utter the words, "I forgive you," we offer them emotional release.

A man came back to work in a place from which he had been fired several months previously. His work was now superior. A fellow worker remembered how inconsistent he had been in the past and asked, "What happened to make such a difference in you?" The man told this story:

"When I was in college, I was part of a fraternity initiation committee. We placed the new members in the middle of a long stretch of country road. I was to drive my car as fast as possible – straight at them. The challenge was for them to stand firm until a signal was given to jump out of the way. It was a dark night. I had reached one hundred miles per hour and saw their looks of terror in the headlights. The signal was given and everyone jumped clear—except one boy.

"I left college after that. I later married and had two children. I became hopelessly inconsistent, moody, and finally became a problem drinker. My wife had to work to bring in the only income we had.

"I was drinking at home one morning when someone rang the doorbell. I opened the door to find myself facing the mother of the boy I had killed years before. She said that she had hated me and spent agonizing nights rehearsing ways to get revenge. She then told me of the love and forgiveness that had come when she gave her heart to Christ. She said, 'I have come to let you know that I forgive you, and I want you to forgive me.'

"I looked into her eyes that morning and saw deep in her eyes the permission to be the kind of man I might have been had I never killed that boy. That forgiveness changed my whole life."[3]

Practical Ways to Forgive One Another

1. **Forgiveness is a choice; it is a function of our wills, not our emotions.**

When we are offended, we must *choose* to forgive because we will seldom *feel* like forgiving. Ephesians 4:31 says, "Get rid of all bitterness, rage and anger." The Greek word for "get rid of" is *airo*, which means "to carry off or take away." When we forgive someone, we "let go of" the offense. It is an act of our will—forgiveness is not an emotion.

That's why we must forgive whether or not we *feel* like forgiving. The truth is, we seldom feel like forgiving those who have hurt us. That's why it must be an act of our will.

And forgiving doesn't always lead to forgetting. I'm often asked, "As an act of my will, I have volitionally and mentally forgiven a person who hurt me deeply; but I just can't forget it nor do I seem to be able to get over it. I thought we were supposed to forgive and forget—but how?"

Yes, we are to forgive, but sometimes it is hard, if not impossible, to forget. You can't erase the memory of a painful event like you can delete a file in your computer.

2. **Forgiveness is a matter of stewardship.**

We are to forgive others because we have been forgiven. Colossians 3:13 says, "Forgive as the Lord forgave you." We are often reluctant to forgive because our offender doesn't "deserve" to be forgiven. The truth is, *no one* deserves to be forgiven; it is one of the manifold graces of God. When we forgive others, we are simply sharing with them some of what God has already given us. If we have difficulty forgiving others, it may be because we have not yet received God's forgiveness, or perhaps we have forgotten about his free gift to us.

> We may forgive, ostensibly to set a prisoner free, only to discover that the prisoner was us.

I counseled a couple whose marriage had been wounded by the husband's infidelity. After a few sessions, he became genuinely remorseful about his sin, got on his knees in front of his wife, and with tears in his eyes, confessed his sin and asked for her forgiveness. I was surprised by her answer. She said, "No." The husband looked up at me, as if to ask, "What do I do now?" I really didn't know what to tell him. We quickly ended that session.

During the week, the Lord spoke to my heart through Colossians 3:13. It occurred to me that perhaps the wife was having a hard time forgiving because she had never received God's forgiveness herself; therefore, she had nothing to offer.

When I met with the couple the following week, I presented the gospel message and asked each of them if he/she had ever asked Christ to be his/her Savior and Lord. He had; she had not. I then asked her if she would like to receive God's gift of eternal life. She said she would. We prayed together in my office that day, and God's amazing grace once again escorted a human soul from the domain of darkness into his marvelous light.

I then shared with her this story from Matthew 18, a story that Jesus told when teaching on forgiveness.

There once was a servant who owed his king ten thousand talents of gold. In today's currency that's several million dollars. He could not pay so the king had him thrown into prison. But the servant appealed to the king and the king was merciful. Not only did he release the man from prison but he also forgave his debt.

The same servant had a slave who owed him a hundred denarii (a few dollars in today's currency). The servant demanded the slave to pay the debt. When he could not, the servant ignored his plea for mercy and had him thrown into prison.

When the king heard about this he was furious. He called the servant in and said, "You wicked servant. I canceled all your debt because you begged me to. Shouldn't you have had mercy on your fellow servant just as I had on you?" The king then turned him over to the jailers until he could pay back all he owed.

The chapter ends with Jesus saying, "This is how my heavenly Father will treat each of you unless you forgive your brother from your heart."

I explained to the wife that in this story the king represents God, the servant represents you and me, and the slave represents those who "owe" us, that is, those who have offended us. The lesson is obvious: Because of our sin, we owed an enormous debt to God that was impossible to pay. We deserved a prison sentence. But God forgave; he canceled our debt. People who have offended us are technically in our debt, but since we have received forgiveness from God, we are free to (and must) cancel the debt they owe us.

I then appealed to her by asking, "Having now received forgiveness from God, would you be willing to share some of it with your husband?"

She did.

Think of some of the areas in which God has forgiven you. Write a short statement expressing your gratitude to God for his having forgiven you.

_____

_____

3. We should forgive whether or not our offender asks our forgiveness.

I'm often asked, "If someone has offended me, shouldn't I wait until he asks my forgiveness before I forgive him?"

The testimony of Jesus will answer this question.

While on the cross Jesus prayed, "Father, forgive them, for they do not know what they're doing" (Luke 23:34). Obviously, at this point, the masses were not asking for forgiveness, but Jesus forgave them nevertheless. Forgiveness is not based on whether our offender deserves our forgiveness or whether he asks for it. We are to forgive because we have been forgiven; it's a matter of stewardship.

Sometimes, it may not even be possible for your offender to ask for your forgiveness. For instance, what if you're seriously injured in a car wreck caused by a drunken driver and the intoxicated driver is killed in the accident? You'll never hear him ask for your forgiveness; the issue is—will you forgive him anyway?

A friend of mine shared this testimony about the importance of forgiving our offenders before they ask for forgiveness. "Several years ago a man really hurt my wife and me deeply. He was not a Christian, so we had difficulty communicating to him about this issue. The problem dragged on for years. Three years later, he showed up at our house one evening and asked if we could talk. We were really surprised when he confessed that what he had done to us years earlier was wrong. He asked our forgiveness. We were deeply touched. We replied, 'Thank you so much for coming tonight. We appreciate what you have said, and we want you to know that we forgave you three years ago when the incident first happened. Yes, you are forgiven.'"

What if this couple had not forgiven their offender until that evening? Chances are, they would have suffered from three years of anger and frustration.

Write about an incident in which someone has wronged you but has never asked your forgiveness.

_____

_____

Have you forgiven this person? If not, would you be willing to do so right now?

_____

When God forgave us, he did so with "no strings attached."

We are to do likewise.

4. We should not make our forgiveness conditional.

When God forgave us, he did so with "no strings attached." We are to do likewise. In other words, we shouldn't say,

- "I'll forgive you if you promise to never do it again."
- "I'll forgive you if you'll clean the house."
- "I'll forgive you, but I'm going to sulk for days."
- "I'll forgive you, but only after I tell everyone what you did."
- "I'll forgive you this time, but not if you do it again."

A good statement of forgiveness never involves "ifs" or "buts."

5. It _is_ acceptable to share with our offender how deeply we were hurt by what happened.

As mentioned above, we should never put conditions on our forgiveness; but it is acceptable, when appropriate, to share with our offender how deeply he hurt us.

The following testimony illustrates why this is acceptable and beneficial:

My husband hurt me deeply when he violated our marriage by having an affair. For months after I found out, he didn't even want to talk about it. But one evening, after we had finished dinner, he walked up to me while I was cleaning the kitchen and said, "Sweetheart, I realize that my being unfaithful to you was wrong. Would you forgive me?"

I was really shocked and confused. On the one hand, I appreciated the fact that he was confessing; but on the other hand, I felt like if I said yes, he'd just walk off and that would be the end of it. I desperately needed to talk this out.

So I replied, "Honey, I appreciate the fact that you've come to me and confessed. But it would mean a lot to me if we could sit down tonight and talk. I really need to share with you the depth of how this has hurt me."

That evening we spent several hours talking. I was able to share with him the depth of my pain, how I had felt betrayed, humiliated, hurt, and disappointed. He listened intently. The more I shared, the more sorrowful he felt over hurting me. I really believe God brought a depth of understanding to my husband during that time that was lacking before. When I finished expressing my hurt, I said, "I forgive you."

As I reflect back on that incident, I realize that I was to forgive him even if we didn't get to talk it out. Actually, I was to forgive him even if he didn't ask for my forgiveness; but being able to share how I was feeling brought great healing to my life and our relationship.

Mom's Investment

 When I began writing this particular section, I tried to think of a time when Mom was reluctant to forgive me—but I can't think of any. I thought about the time I wrecked the car, the times I disobeyed, but she was always quick to forgive; she never held a grudge. I never sensed any condemnation from her. I thought about her relationship with Dad; he was very hard to live with. Again, no memories of outburst of anger, resentment, or bitterness. I analyzed another situation that was very hurtful to Mom. A close relative refused my mother's love for many years. Mom kept loving, this individual continued to shun and neglect. After Mom died, one day I was reading her prayer journal when I saw these prayers: "1981—I asked the Lord to help me forget someone who did not return my love, but he said, "No, you continue to love her." A later entry read, "You cannot make someone love you, but she cannot keep you from loving her." That was Mom—quick to forgive, and slow to hold a grudge.

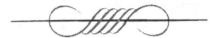

A little boy came to the Washington Monument and noticed a guard standing by it. The little boy looked up at the guard and said, "I want to buy it." The guard stooped down and said, "How much do you have?" The boy reached into his pocket and pulled out a quarter. The guard said, "That's not enough." The boy replied, "I thought you would say that." So he pulled out nine cents more. The guard looked down at the boy and said, "You need to understand three things. First, the thirty-four cents is not enough. In fact, thirty-four million dollars is not enough to buy the Washington Monument. Second, the Washington Monument is not for sale. And third, if you are an American citizen, the Washington Monument already belongs to you."[4]

We need to understand three things about forgiveness. First, we cannot earn it. Second, it is not for sale. And third, if we have simply asked Christ, we already have it.

Write your own definition of Forgive One Another.

_____

_____

_____

Personal Journal

1. Write about a time in your life when someone forgave you and it impacted you deeply.

_____

_____

2. Who has hurt you the most in life? Have you forgiven this person?

_____

_____

3. Write down some ways in which other people have hurt you. In order to bring emotional resolution to these issues, share them with your OA Partner and allow him or her to comfort you over the pain and loss associated with these incidences. Then, forgive these people who hurt you.

Offender   Offense

_____   _____

_____   _____

_____   _____

_____   _____

_____   _____

4. On a scale from 1 to10 (1 being, "I need to greatly improve" and 10 being, "I do a good job"), how good are you at forgiving people? Ask your OA partner to rate you.

I rated myself a _____.

My OA partner rated me a _____.

Practical Suggestion #7

A church should strive to have each of its members learn and practice the One Anothers.

Imagine what would happen in a church, regardless of its size, if every child, student, and adult had a working knowledge of the One Anothers and practiced them daily. It would revolutionize the church and its impact on its community. The church would enjoy the same favor of the Lord the early church experienced: "They broke bread in their homes and ate together with glad and sincere hearts, praising God and enjoying the favor of all the people. And the Lord added to their number daily those who were being saved" (Acts 2:46–47). The church would become a healthy body and it would enjoy a new momentum in growth.

Additionally, when we learn how to minister the One Anothers, we learn how to "do" Hebrews 10:24: "Let us consider how we may spur one another on toward love and good deeds." Throughout this workbook, we've been "considering."

There are several ways you can use the 11th Commandment material to "spur others toward love and good deeds."

> Imagine what would happen in a church, regardless of its size, if every child, student, and adult had a working knowledge of the One Anothers and practiced them daily.

1. Help establish and develop an 11th Commandment ministry in your church.

An 11th Commandment ministry in the local church is an ongoing ministry that has one simple goal: to encourage every member of the church to experience and share the One Anothers. Nine-week courses can be offered year-round until every member has participated. The course can also become a part of new-member orientation and training. You can be involved in this on-going ministry by serving as:

- A small group leader—facilitates a group of three to five persons. No prior training is necessary although a two-hour orientation session is recommended (led by the class facilitator or the director).
- Class facilitator—leads a class consisting of two or more groups. Receives training at an 11th Commandment training seminar.
- Director of the 11th Commandment ministry in your church—coordinates the overall strategy of the local church ministry. Receives training and certification at an 11th Commandment training seminar.

Also, when you complete this course, encourage fellow church members to enroll in a course.

2. Encourage your church to host an 11th Commandment Seminar.

This four-hour seminar will help "jump-start" an 11th Commandment ministry in your church. The seminar is fast-paced, interactive, engaging, and fun. It introduces the basic concepts of the course and gives an overview of the eight One Anothers that are covered in the first workbook.

3. After completing the 11th Commandment—Book One, complete Book Two.

The second volume discusses in detail eight more of the One Anothers that are briefly mentioned in the last chapter of this workbook (Wait for—Offer Hospitality to—Pray for—Rejoice with—Be Kind to—Honor—Confess Your Sins to—Be Devoted to).

To learn more about the 11th Commandment books, contact the ministry office at (972) 432-8690.

Powerful Result #7

God will reward us for ministering the One Anothers.

There are many benefits to ministering the One Anothers, one of which is that God will reward us. While this reason shouldn't be our primary motivation, nevertheless, it is true. Consider these verses:

- "God is not unjust; *he will not forget your work* and the love you have shown him as you have helped his people and continue to help them" (Hebrews 6:10; emphasis added).

- "Do not merely listen to the word, and so deceive yourselves. Do what it says. . . But the man who looks intently into the perfect law that gives freedom, and continues to do this, not forgetting what he has heard, but doing it—*he will be blessed* in what he does" (James 1:22, 25; emphasis added).

- "Give *and it will be given to you.* A good measure, pressed down, shaken together and running over, will be poured into your lap" (Luke 6:38; emphasis added).

- "But when you give to the needy, do not let your left hand know what your right hand is doing, so that your giving may be in secret. Then your Father, who sees what is done in secret, *will reward you*" (Matthew 6:3; emphasis added).

- "Behold, I am coming soon! *My reward is with me*, and I will give to everyone according to what he has done" (Revelation 22:12; emphasis added).

In Chapter 1, I mentioned that we should never give to someone with the expectation that he or she will reciprocate. While this is true, it is equally true that God rewards those who distribute his divine commodities.

How does he reward us? I'm not even going to get into the how's and the why's, but just know that he will.

Group Time—Session Eight

Each member of the group should give his or her individual response to the first three questions. Allow about two minutes for each person's response. Allow all group members to share their answer to question #1 before proceeding to question #2.

1. What was the most interesting concept in this chapter?

2. Referring back to last week's lesson, share about a time this week when you were able to carry someone's burden and a time when you should have carried someone's burden but did not.

3. Share your responses to the first three Personal Journal entries in this chapter (page 106).

As a group, process these discussion questions: [These discussion questions have been prioritized. Depending on the time allotted for your group discussion, you may not be able to process all the questions.]

    a.   According to Matthew 18:21–22, how many times are we to forgive someone who has offended us? Are you currently involved in a relationship in which someone continually offends you?

    b.   Read Luke 23:34. What can we learn from Jesus' statement of forgiveness?

    c.   What has been your greatest experience of receiving God's forgiveness?

    d.   How will Forgiving One Another be a testimony to "all men" (John 13:34) that we belong to the Lord and that we are his disciples?

    e.   Read Matthew 18:23–35 and discuss the following issues:

- In this story, whom does the king represent? The servant? The fellow servant?
- Why should the servant have forgiven his fellow servant?
- Why didn't the servant forgive his fellow servant?
- What was the final condition of the servant who refused to forgive?
- How did Jesus apply this story to the lives of those who were listening (v. 35)?

    f.   On a scale from 1 to 10 (1 being, "We're not too good at this" and 10 being, "We're really good at this"), how good is your church/organization at forgiving people?

Homework:
Complete chapter 9.

ADMONISH ONE ANOTHER

"Admonish one another with all wisdom" (Colossians 3:16).

Years ago I met a young businessman who aspired to be in the ministry. We began to spend a lot of time together both socially and in ministry. Randy became like a son to me. I would humorously but affectionately call him my "young Timothy," and he would refer to me as his "Paul," referring of course, to the mentoring relationship these two men had.

Through the course of four or five years, we ministered to each other in many ways. I had not yet written the 11th Commandment book so I wasn't totally aware of all the many aspects of ministry that two people can have to one another, but in retrospect we shared most of the One Anothers. We encouraged, comforted, supported, greeted, etc. each other on a regular basis.

Early on in the relationship I noticed a few "loose ends" in his character and lifestyle. They seemed to be minor issues, so I initially brushed them off as youthful immaturity. But they persisted and even got worse.

I am not, by nature, a confrontational person; it was even a challenge for me to discipline my own two daughters (fortunately, they didn't need a lot of discipline). My wife, on the other hand, is a very insightful, forthright person and can quickly discern when something is wrong. So Mary would often say to me, "Don, you really need to confront Randy on some of these issues." While I generally agreed with her, I was hesitant to take her advice.

One day, when Randy and I were having lunch together, he told me that he was seeing a psychologist about some problems he was having. At that moment, I realized that I had neglected my friend. I have absolutely nothing against someone receiving counsel from a professional; it's just that I too should have been available to help my friend work through these problems.

Several months later, Randy seemed to disappear off the face of the earth. For several months I didn't know where he was. At times I was angry with him ("Why doesn't he at least call?"), but most of the time I was just hurt.

Then I found out that he was in jail. Those "loose ends" in his character had gotten out of control and became a first-degree offense.

At that moment I realized I had failed my friend. I had not loved him deeply because I had neglected to admonish him.

I share this painful story because the Lord used this incident in my life to teach me a valuable lesson: If we truly love someone, we must be willing to admonish him. Yes, we should comfort, support, encourage, and prefer, but we must also rebuke and admonish. If we're not willing to Admonish One Another, our love is out of balance and incomplete.

There are two Greek words that are translated into our English word *admonish*. *Noutheteo* means "to warn, to put in mind, to caution or reprove gently." It is used of instruction and warning. *Paraineo* means "to admonish by way of exhorting or advising" (see Acts 27:9).

I share this painful story because the Lord used this incident in my life
to teach me a valuable lesson:
If we truly love someone, we must be willing to admonish him.

Based on these two Greek words, there are two different reasons to admonish.

First, we should warn, caution and gently reprove someone who is in sin or may be heading in the wrong direction:

- "Jane, I think you're getting too emotionally involved with your boyfriend."
- "Jack, you're not spending enough time with your wife."
- "Henry, if you take that new job you'll be traveling 90 percent of the time. That's going to hurt your family."
- "Suzy, it seems like you're slacking off at work."

Second, we should instruct others (admonish them) with the truths of God's Word so that they might benefit from the life and freedom that comes from the truth (John 8:32). There is another One Another that has a similar meaning—Colossians 3:16 tells us to Teach One Another. In other words, admonishing is not just something we do when someone has messed up but also when they need to be taught and/or warned:

- "Son, now that you're twelve years old, let me teach you the blessings of moral purity."
- "James, since you're a new Christian, allow me to share with you the principles of the Spirit filled life."
- "Lauren, now that you have your first full-time job, let's learn what the Bible teaches about financial stewardship."

Admonishing others is also to be distinguished from rebuking others, which is certainly biblical (Luke 17:3; Titus 1:13), but rebuking implies a harsher treatment. Jesus rebuked evil spirits

(Matthew 17:18), fever (Luke 4:39), the wind (Matthew 8:26), and on several occasions, his disciples (Mark 8:33; Luke 9:55).

As a general rule, before we admonish someone, we should first minister the other One Anothers to him. Once we have preferred, encouraged, comforted, and accepted someone, we have then earned the right to admonish him. If we attempt to admonish someone prior to caring for him, our ministry will likely be repelled.

The old parenting formula [enforcing rules without relationship = rebellion] is sound advice.

For instance, in 2 Thessalonians 3, the apostle Paul issued a rather stern admonition, "We hear that some among you are idle. They are not busy; they are busybodies. If a man will not work, he shall not eat" (vs. 11, 10). That's tough language—get off your duff and go to work or don't eat. How did Paul get away with speaking to the church at Thessalonica like that? Perhaps the answer is seen in his first letter to the Thessalonian church. In his first letter we read, "As apostles of Christ we could have been a burden to you, but we were gentle among you, like a mother caring for her little children. We loved you so much that we were delighted to share with you not only the gospel of God but our lives as well, because you had become so dear to us" (1 Thessalonians 2:8). Paul had earned the right to speak bluntly because he had first loved them dearly. His gentleness preceded his admonition. The church received his rebuke because they were convinced of his love.

> A recent survey indicated that the average American father spends only seventeen minutes a week with each of his children. And for thirteen of those seventeen minutes, the father is disciplining his child.

A recent survey indicated that the average American father spends only seventeen minutes a week with each of his children. And for thirteen of those seventeen minutes, the father is disciplining his child. To begin with, seventeen minutes out of 10,080 minutes in the week is not a lot of time. It's hard to convince your child that you really care for her if you only spend seventeen minutes a week with her. But notice that thirteen of the seventeen minutes are spent in discipline and correction. Our children must be thinking, *Dad doesn't spend much time with me and when he does, he's in my face, telling me what I'm doing that's wrong.* It's no wonder that our children are often rebellious. We've lost the balance of Hebrews 12:6: "The Lord disciplines those he loves." We try to discipline our children prior to genuinely loving them.

Several years ago we had a situation in our church that was similar to the situation in the church at Thessalonica. One of our members wasn't providing for his family. He would not commit himself to a steady job, and his inconsistency was creating a terrific hardship on his family. I just happened to be working on this chapter during that time, so, wanting to abide by the general principle of "love first, then discipline," I made a concerted effort to befriend this man. I met with him on several occasions for fellowship and prayer, and Mary and I had him and his wife over to the house one evening for dinner. After I was convinced that he knew I loved him and cared for him, I met with him one day and in a kind but direct way told him, "Go get a job."

I realize that there may be times when we need to admonish someone, and there's not the time nor opportunity to develop the preferred groundwork. For instance, if we hear that a man is about to abandon his wife and family, a quick intervention is probably necessary; there may not be time to establish the depth of loving relationship we would want. But those times should be infrequent.

Practical Suggestions on Admonishing Others

When we admonish someone, we should be very careful how we do it. I usually don't put much forethought and planning into how I'm going to prefer, support, or comfort someone; I just do it. Those three One Anothers "feel so good" to the recipient that it's hard to mess up how you dispense them. I've never offended someone by trying to support him. No one has ever gotten mad at me for comforting him.

But admonishing is different. That's why 2 Timothy 4:2 says to do so carefully, "Correct, rebuke and encourage—*with great patience and careful instruction*" (emphasis added). It's like the difference between driving down miles of straight, open highway and driving in the mountains. When we're on the open highway, we can put the car on cruise control and take a mental hike. But in the mountains, we better slow down, focus, and continually adjust to the changing terrain. Most of the One Anothers can be dispensed without much consideration or precaution. But when we need to admonish someone, we should carefully consider issues such as:

- Does this person indeed need to be admonished?
- Am I the right person to do it?
- When would be the best time to admonish him?
- Does this person know that I love him?

Here are a few guidelines and precautions to consider before admonishing someone.

1. Before admonishing someone, make sure you're not guilty of the same problem.

In Matthew 7:3–5, Jesus teaches, "Do not judge, or you too will be judged. For in the same way you judge others, you will be judged, and with the measure you use, it will be measured to you. Why do you look at the speck of dust in your brother's eye and pay no attention to the plank in your own eye? How can you say to your brother, 'Let me take the speck out of your eye,' When all the time there is a plank in your own eye? You hypocrite, first take the plank out of your own eye, and then you will see clearly to remove the speck from your brother's eye."

For sure, don't try to admonish someone about an issue with which you struggle. Don't admonish someone about eating too much if you're overweight. Don't correct someone about talking too much if you struggle with the same.

But I think this passage also speaks to a more general theme: Before you admonish or correct someone, search your own heart to see if there is anything the Lord is wanting to admonish you about. The Lord may deal with you about an entirely different issue than what you are going to address in the other person.

If we're careful to take the plank out of our own eye first, we'll have more confidence in our ministry to others.

2. Make sure your admonition is based on Scripture, not just on your personal beliefs or opinions.

It's important that we base our admonition on Scripture instead of a personal belief, opinion, or preference. Can you sense the difference between these statements?

- "Sally, when you talk to people, you get too excited. I don't like it when you get all revved up."
- "Roger, sometimes you make cutting remarks to those of us who work with you. To you, it may be humorous, but some of what you say really hurts me. Ephesians 5:4 says that we are to avoid any type of course language or foolish talk."
- "John, you shouldn't be working for a landscape company. You have more potential than that. You could make a lot more money doing something else."
- "Thomas, it would be best if you didn't take that job that will require you to be gone from your family all during the week. You have young children who need you and so

does your wife. In 1 Timothy 5, the apostle Paul says that God is pleased when we care for our own family. I'm concerned that your new work schedule would cause you to neglect your family."

When using Scripture to admonish someone, it's *important not to use it as a sledgehammer.*

Don't be heavy-handed with God's Word.

The statements made to Sally and John are personal opinions and preferences. While it is okay to share our opinions with others, this is not the same as admonishing someone based on Scripture, and we should be careful to explain the difference. Even the apostle Paul was careful to distinguish between his own personal convictions and what he had received from the Lord:

- Personal conviction—"Now about virgins; I have no command from the Lord, but I give a judgment" (1 Corinthians 7:25).
- Biblical absolute—"According to the Lord's own words, we tell you" (1 Thessalonians 4:15).

The statements made to Roger and Thomas are based on a particular scripture. Of course, Roger and Thomas might disagree as to whether these particular scriptures apply to them, but at least there is a biblical basis for discussion, not just a whimsical set of preferences.

Indeed, God has given us his Word as a resource for admonishing others: "Preach the Word; be prepared in season and out of season; correct, rebuke and encourage" (2 Timothy 4:2). "All Scripture is God-breathed and is useful for teaching, rebuking, correcting and training in righteousness" (2 Timothy 3:16).

When using Scripture to admonish someone, it's important not to use it as a sledgehammer. Don't be heavy-handed with God's Word. Be gentle and subtle when introducing Scripture into a tense conversation.

3. Pray for the person, and yourself, before you go to him.

First, pray that the person will change without you having to confront him: "Now we pray to God that you will not do anything wrong" (2 Corinthians 13:7). This may mean that you pray for this individual for an extended period of time prior to going to him.

Second, pray that the person you feel led to admonish will be open to you and that she will receive what you have to say: "I pray that the eyes of your heart may be enlightened" (Ephesians 1:18).

Also, pray for yourself, that your motives will be pure in confronting this person and that you will do so in the power of the Spirit: "Search me, O God, and know my heart; test me and know my anxious thoughts. See if there is any offensive way in me, and lead me in the way everlasting" (Psalm 139: 23–24).

4. Pray about the right *time* and *place* to approach the individual.

The writer of Ecclesiastes emphasized the importance of proper timing. He said there is a proper time for everything, including a "time to be silent and a time to speak" (Ecclesiastes 3:7).

Paul also taught that we should be sensitive to timing whenever we have something to say, "Let no unwholesome word proceed out of your mouth but only such a word as is good for edification, *according to the need of the moment*" (Ephesians 4:29 NASB; emphasis added). When admonishing someone, a major point of sensitivity is the timing factor. Some variables might include: Which day of the week is best? What time of day is best? What will this person be doing after the meeting? (For instance, you wouldn't want to have a potentially tense meeting with someone right before he is to teach a Bible study class.)

Another point of sensitivity involves determining the proper place. It might be best to approach the person in his own environment so that after the meeting he is already in a comfortable setting. But, it may be best to meet at a neutral location.

The basic guideline should be, "What time and place is best for the individual I'm going to talk to? What will make him the most comfortable?"

5. Approach the person privately.

Matthew 18:15 teaches, "If your brother sins against you, go and show him his fault, just between the two of you."

> "How would you like a job where, if you make a mistake, a big red light goes on and eighteen thousand people boo?"

I believe that the spirit of this verse also teaches that we shouldn't even share with others what we are going to share with an individual until we have first gone to him in private. In other words, if we talk to everyone in the church about how a brother is sinning, even if we do go to him in private—we have violated this verse. Furthermore, if we go to this individual and he receives what we share, we should not even tell anyone that we met with him.

The person we are visiting with will highly value our discretion and confidentiality. Former hockey goalie Jacques Plante once said, "How would you like a job where, if you make a mistake, a big red light goes on and eighteen thousand people boo?"

Hockey players don't like it, and neither do we.

6. Make sure your actions are properly motivated.

The main motivation behind admonishing someone should be that you love him and want the best for him as opposed to thoughts of revenge, anger, or wanting to humiliate him. In Acts 20:31, we read that the apostle Paul warned the church at Ephesus "with tears." His warning was obviously motivated by a deep love for them. He told the Corinthians, "I am not writing this to shame you, but to warn you, as my dear children" (1 Corinthians 4:14).

So we must ask, "*Why* am I going to admonish this person? What thoughts and feelings are motivating me?"

According to 2 Timothy 3:16, the end result of admonishing should be that we will be "thoroughly equipped for every good work." So our primary motivation for admonishing someone is that he might be better equipped for Kingdom business.

7. Admonish gently.

"Brothers, if someone is caught in a sin, you who are spiritual should restore him gently" (Galatians 6:1). "Do not rebuke an older man harshly, but exhort him as if he were your father" (1 Timothy 5:1).

As a general rule, people are sensitive. We can treat inanimate objects brusquely, but when we deal with people, we must be tactful, diplomatic, and sensitive. This suggestion applies to all human interaction but particularly to the ministry of admonishing others.

Initially, we may be angry with the person who needs to be admonished because what he is doing is wrong and has hurt others and us. But before we actually admonish the person, we need to settle down and focus on how we want to *love* this individual. It's best not to admonish someone when we're frustrated, angry, and stirred up. Emotionally, we need to be calm.

We also need to craft our words carefully; a measure of tact and diplomacy is always helpful. This reminds me of the insurance sales manager who was known for his tact and diplomacy. One of his young salesmen was performing so poorly that he had to be terminated. The manager called him in and said, "Son, I don't know how we're ever going to get along without you, but starting Monday we're going to try."

Be gentle both in *what* is said and *how* you say it; that is, consider your tone of voice. People often are affected more by *how* something is communicated than they are by what is said.

8. **The admonition should be clear, accurate, and thorough.**

While it is important that we admonish gently, it is also important to be clear, accurate, and thorough.

Be clear. Try to condense the admonition into one or two statements: "Jane, you're often late to work." "Richard, you need to get a job and support your family." "Sarah, you're neglecting your children."

Give examples: "Jane, last week you were late to work two out of five days." "Richard, you haven't had a steady job in ten months." "Sarah, you only see your children one night a week."

Be accurate. Don't exaggerate. "Jane, you're always late." "Richard, you're totally lazy." "Sarah, your kids don't even know who you are."

Don't base your statements on assumption. "Jane, I don't see you in your office first thing in the morning, so I just assume you're not here." "Richard, because you no longer work for Cargill, I assume you have no steady source of income." "Sarah, I know you're busy these days, so I just assume that your kids are suffering because of it."

Be thorough. Often, in our attempt to be gentle, we may be less than thorough in what we need to say. Once we have begun to admonish someone, it's best to "get it all out on the table."

This doesn't mean we should confront someone on every minor and major issue that needs to be addressed in his life—all at once. It is often best to address one issue at a time, but cover that one issue thoroughly. Don't hedge on what needs to be said. People would prefer to have the entire load all at once rather than to get part of it one day, part of it the next, and the final residue a week later. Admonishing someone can be an uncomfortable and even an unpleasant experience, so it's best to thoroughly deal with a situation in one setting.

There's almost something frustrating about someone who is quick to tell us what we're doing *wrong but offers no suggestions as to how to correct the situation.*

---

9. **When we admonish someone, we should not only tell him *what* to do but *how* to do it, and, if possible, be willing to journey with him through the process.**

The goal of admonishing someone is restoration and/or change. Something is amiss that needs to be corrected. So to be thorough in our ministry of admonition, we need to not only state what is wrong, but also to suggest positive steps of action that will help solve the problem. For instance, if we admonish a father relative to his unruly children, we also need to share with him biblical principles of parenting. There's almost something frustrating about someone who is quick to tell us what we're doing wrong but offers no suggestions as to how to correct the situation.

Furthermore, if possible, after we have admonished someone and suggested corrective steps, we should be involved in the restoration process. For instance, I admonished a friend about his financial irresponsibility but then proceeded to teach him how a budget works, and we set up a system of accountability. I admonished a friend about her lack of compassion and then spent time with her, studying what the Bible says about mercy and compassion and then continued to "monitor" the compassion factor for the next year or two.

The apostle Paul admonished the Corinthian church relative to sexual immorality but then taught them on the subject and even helped them work through a particular situation involving an immoral incident within the church (1 Corinthians 5–6).

I realize that it's not always possible to be involved in the follow-up process, but we should certainly try.

10. **Be careful not to be influenced by the person needing to be admonished or by his sin: "Restore him gently. But watch yourself, or you also may be tempted" (Galatians 6:1).**

Admonishing someone usually involves talking about and dealing with sin. And sin is very deceitful (Hebrews 3:13). That's why Paul warns us to be careful whenever we are, in any way, dealing with sin. At best, we may be tempted; at worst, we may engage in the very sin that we are reproving.

For instance, it's often best not to discuss the details of a situation, particularly if it involves a moral issue, because it is disgraceful even to speak of such things.

Early in my ministry, I counseled a single man who was having severe immorality problems. He was entangled in pornography and fornication. In our first session, he went into graphic detail regarding his involvement. I heard things I had no need to hear. In our next session, I told him to stick to the general problem and not to discuss the details.

11. **Subsequent to admonishing someone, at a different time and in a different setting, contact him again to reassure him of your love for him.**

Admonishing someone may cause him to become insecure regarding the relationship. He may wonder, *Does Don still love me? Is our relationship going to be different now that this issue has come up? Is he mad at me?* Satan can use these thoughts to foster self-doubt in the individual and unwarranted strain in the relationship. To prevent this from happening, following the time of admonition, meet with the person you have admonished for the expressed purpose of reassuring him that you still love him and that you're committed to the health of the relationship.

Sometimes just a hug or handshake and a simple, "Randy, I love you and value our relationships" is sufficient. At other times, a longer exchange may be needed.

This is what the apostle Paul instructed the Corinthian church to do when the "brother who is in sin" (as identified in 1 Corinthians 5:1–5) repented. In his second letter to the Corinthian church, Paul instructed the members to forgive, comfort and reaffirm their love for him (2 Corinthians 2:7–8).

12. Be careful not to minister shame or condemnation to the person you are admonishing.

When the apostle Paul admonished the church in Corinth, he was careful to clarify his intent: "I am not writing this to shame you, but to warn you" (1 Corinthians 4:14).

While we have every right to warn and admonish someone, we must never shame or condemn him. Condemnation makes me feel like I am a bad person; I begin to think that there is something significantly wrong with me as a person.

> Address the action without attacking the person.

When admonishing someone, don't hesitate to clearly state the problem ("You told a lie."), but don't exaggerate the problem and begin to infer that the *individual* is the problem ("You're a liar. You're incapable of telling the truth."). Address the action without attacking the person.

Sometimes, when needing to admonish someone, I will picture the person in my mind and then imagine that she has a small blemish on her face, perhaps a bit of dirt. This helps me to visualize that although there is something that needs to be addressed and cleared up, it is but a small part of her overall personage.

So when admonishing someone, keep things in perspective; don't speak in such a way as to denigrate who he is as a person.

13. Realize that, initially, your admonition may hurt the person you're admonishing but in the end, it will benefit him and strengthen your relationship.

In his first letter to the church at Corinth, the apostle Paul strongly admonished them because of sexual sin that was being tolerated in the church (see 1 Corinthians 5). In his second letter, he followed–up on his admonition by saying, "Even if I caused you sorrow by my letter, I do not regret it. Though I did regret it—I see that my letter hurt you, but only for a little while—yet now I am happy, not because you were made sorry, but because your sorrow led you to repentance" (2 Corinthians 7:8-9).

Paul realized that, "No discipline seems pleasant at the time, but painful. Later on, however, it produces a harvest of righteousness and peace for those who have been trained by it" (Hebrews 12:11).

Practical Ways to *Receive* the Ministry of Admonition

We've talked a lot about admonishing others; let's spend a little time discussing how we should react when someone admonishes us. First, some ground rules:

1. Be approachable.

Tell the people you are close to, that if you offend them, you want them to approach you and talk it out. Give them permission to "[speak] the truth in love" with you (Ephesians 4:15). For instance, you could say: "When I do something that hurts you, or if you misunderstand something I do or say, please come to me and share the truth in love. I promise to receive you and listen to what you have to say."

To be approachable doesn't mean you must change your mind or position to concur with whomever is approaching you. But being approachable means that people should always feel the freedom to come and talk to you.

Do people perceive you as someone who is approachable? If not, why not? Have you proactively given people permission to approach you?

_____

_____

2. **Realize that being admonished usually doesn't initially "feel good," but it is good for us.**

"No discipline seems pleasant at the time, but painful. Later on, it produces a harvest of righteousness and peace for those who have been trained by it" (Hebrews 12:11). We may feel uncomfortable during the process, but we should realize that it will bring about a good result.

3. **Realize that sometimes when people admonish us, they may not do it just right.**

"Our fathers disciplined us for a little while as they thought best" (Hebrews 12:10). When people admonish us, they may violate some of the suggestions given earlier in this chapter and/or they may be wrong (or partially wrong) in what they are saying. But we should still be open to what they have to say.

Practical Ways to *Respond* to Someone Who Is Admonishing You

1. **Listen attentively to what is being said.**

Poor listening has been defined as "Thinking about what I'm going to say, to refute what you are saying, as soon as I get a chance to break into the conversation." To the contrary, we should be quiet and listen attentively to the admonition. Listen to what the person is saying and to what the Holy Spirit may be saying to you. After the person is through presenting his admonition, try to verbally clarify what you think he said by reflecting back to him a summary of his concerns. For instance, "John, what I hear you saying is that you think I should be more discreet with information that people share with me."

2. **Thank the person for his ministry.**

Affirm the fact that you realize what is going on (you're being admonished) and that you are open to this process. "John, I realize that you are concerned about this issue, and I thank you for taking the time to talk to me about it."

3. **In a non-defensive manner, discuss the issue.**

There's nothing wrong with asking for clarification of what is being said or even to ask for examples. And, it is acceptable to politely disagree with what is being said, although if this is done immediately, defensively, or dogmatically it may short-circuit the ministry of admonition. Proverbs 18:17 says, "The first to present his case seems right, till another comes forward and questions him"—which, in our vernacular means, "There are usually two sides to every story."

4. **Receive the truth.**

When someone admonishes us, we need to try to hear what he is saying (and what the Holy Spirit is wanting to say), and receive the truth, even though what is said may not be 100 percent accurate in content or delivery. Even if we disagree with what is being said we should have the attitude, "If 90 percent of what is being said is wrong and 10 percent is right, I want to hear and receive the 10 percent."

5. **In a gracious way, verbally respond to the admonition.**

   At the close of the session, respond to the admonition. Depending on how much of the admonition you agree with, your response may be worded in several ways:
   - If you don't agree with what has been said, you could say, "Thank you for taking the time to visit with me. I always want to be open to what you and others want to say to me. I promise to prayerfully consider what you have said."
   - If you do agree with what has been said, you could say, "Thank you for taking the time to visit with me. What you have shared makes a lot of sense and I receive what you say. Pray with me and for me, that I will be open to God's work in my life."

6. **Don't confuse the conversation by introducing areas that you think are wrong in the life of the person who is admonishing you.**

   When confronted with an area that needs to be changed in our lives, our general tendency is to respond by introducing an area that may need to be addressed in the life of the person who is admonishing us.
   - "Yeah, well, I may have a problem with being discreet with information that I know about others, but you have a sever problem with your temper. You're always losing your cool over the smallest issues."

   While your assessment may be correct, this is not the time to bring it up. You may need to prayerfully consider initiating the Admonish One Another process with this person at a later date.

   At this particular time, the focus is on you; don't try to deflect the focus to someone else or onto another issue.

7. **If what you are being admonished about is actually an issue of sin and you are convicted that the admonition is correct, confess the sin to God (1 John 1:9) and to those who have been affected (James 5:16) and ask forgiveness.**

   If we are confronted about a sin issue and we are indeed wrong, to simply acknowledge the wrong is insufficient; we need to ask forgiveness: "John, you're right. I have been indiscreet with information that people have shared with me and that has no doubt caused confusion, disillusionment, distrust and a lot of hurt. I have been wrong. Please forgive me. I will also call those whom I have wronged and ask for their forgiveness."

8. **End the session with prayer.**

   If appropriate, both parties should pray.

9. **When someone correctly admonishes us, we should esteem him, not resent him.**

   First Thessalonians 5:12–13 says to, "Respect those who work hard among you, who are over you in the Lord and who admonish you. Hold them in the highest regard in love because of their work."

   After the meeting is over, protect your heart from thoughts of resentment toward the person who admonished you. Instead, respect, honor and esteem him. In prayer, thank God for the person's ministry in your life. If appropriate, write the person a note of appreciation or speak a word of appreciation. Chances are, the person who admonished you may have felt very insecure about doing so and he may be worried that the incident will adversely affect your relationship. So make every effort to "reconnect" with the person in order to reaffirm the relationship.

If we are confronted about a sin issue and we are indeed wrong, to simply acknowledge the wrong is insufficient;

we need to ask forgiveness.

The Scope of Admonishing Someone

The preceding information may tend to suggest that admonishing someone must be a "big deal"—a formal, premeditated meeting complete with agenda, Power Point presentation, handouts, etc. While at times a formal meeting may be appropriate and necessary, admonishing others can also take on a more relaxed, casual, almost impromptu approach. For instance, we may need to casually say to an employee who arrives late to work, "Jane, try to be on time to work." If your child neglects to do his chores, don't wait to have a big meeting, just say, "Joey, you haven't taken out the trash. You can't go play baseball until you do."

Mom's Investment

■ I have always been reluctant to admonish others. I avoid confrontation. It wasn't until I began to write this workbook that I realized why. ■ In each chapter I have been sharing a way in which my mother ministered a particular One Another to me. This is to substantiate my theory that we must first receive these grace gifts before we can give them. Through the years I have known what encouragement looked like because my mother was a constant source of encouragement. I can say the same about most of the other One Anothers. But not about Admonish One Another. I can't honestly think of a time in my life when my mother admonished me. I remember many times when my father scolded me or tried to shame me, but that's entirely different. I suppose the one way in which my mother's love was lacking is that she was reluctant to admonish me. ■ And that's why, through the years, I've been reluctant to admonish others. I just didn't know how it sounded or how it felt. Nor did I sense the love that flows from a gentle, kind admonition. ■ Fortunately, there were others who sometimes met that need. In my last year of college, I remember receiving a kind letter from a childhood friend, warning me about the dangers of immorality (my girlfriend and I were sorely tempted in this area). A few times, pastors whom I have worked with have lovingly spoken to me about specific areas of concern. ■ I can also remember times when people felt compelled to correct me but really botched it. They essentially violated all the suggestions listed earlier in this chapter. They caused me to feel a lot of shame and condemnation. ■ I'll end this chapter by simply reiterating the two major issues we've discussed: If you're going to love someone thoroughly, you must be willing to admonish him, but for heaven's sake (and his), be careful how you do it.

Personal Journal

1. Write about a time in your life when someone lovingly admonished you.

   _____

   How did you receive the admonition?

   _____

   Did the admonition eventually help make you a better person?

   _____

2. When was the last time you admonished someone?

   _____

   Based on the practical suggestions listed above, analyze how you handled the situation: What did you do right? What could you have done better?

   _____

   Ways in which I could have done better:

   _____

3. Are there people in your life who feel the freedom to admonish you? Are you accountable to anyone for your continued Christian growth?

   _____

   List their names:

   _____

4. Is confronting others hard for you to do? Why?

   _____

5. Think of someone you know that you're concerned about who might need the ministry of admonition. After reviewing the practical suggestions listed above, prayerfully consider admonishing him.

6. On a scale from 1 to 10 (1 being, "I need to greatly improve" and 10 being, "I do a good job"), how well are you admonishing others? Ask your OA Partner to rate you.

   I rated myself a _____.
   My OA partner rated me a _____.

Practical Suggestion #8

Love is something you do

Love is a verb—an action verb. In order to truly love someone, I must *do* something. If I continually tell someone, "I love you" but never demonstrate my love, my declaration soon becomes shallow, trite and even offensive.

A well-known passage from Luke's Gospel illustrates the importance of the active dimension of love.

A lawyer asked Jesus, "Teacher, what must I do to inherit eternal life?" Jesus answered his question with a question, "What is written in the Law?" The lawyer must have been in the crowd the day Jesus declared what we call the Great Commandment, because he answered, "Love the Lord your God and love your neighbor as yourself." To which Jesus replied, "You have answered correctly, do this and you will live." The lawyer wanted further clarification, "And who is my neighbor?" Jesus answered this question by telling a story that we call the parable of the Good Samaritan. It's interesting to note that in the story, Jesus not only clarifies *who* our neighbor is, but he also illustrates *what we can do* to love our neighbor.

If you're not familiar with the details of the story, read Luke 10:30–35. You'll notice the answer to these two questions:

1. Who is our neighbor?—Someone who has a need.

*2. What can we **do** to love our neighbor?*

- Have compassion on him (v. 33)— Comfort One Another
- Stop what we're doing and minister to him (v. 34)—Prefer One Another
- Minister to his physical needs (v. 34)— Serve One Another
- Personally care for him (v. 34)—Care for One Another
- Use our resources to help someone (v. 35)—Carry One Another's Burdens
- Minister to him for the long-term (v. 35)—Be Devoted to One Another

Jesus' parable teaches how we are to "Love your neighbor as yourself" but it also includes an illustration of how to neglect loving your neighbor. Notice that there are three possible caregivers in this story: a priest, a Levite and the Samaritan. The priest and Levite saw the man in need but did nothing. The Samaritan took action.

Love is something you do.

It's interesting to note that Jesus used two religious men to illustrate neglect. Perhaps they were engaged in a ministerial assignment—too busy to get practical. It's also interesting to note that Jesus used a Samaritan to illustrate what genuine love looks like. Jews thought that Samaritans were worthless, but Jesus rebuked their prejudice by making a Samaritan the hero of the story. In essence Jesus said, "It's not those who merely talk about religion that are fulfilling the Great Commandment, it's those who do something."

The apostle John spoke the identical truth in 1 John 3:18: "Dear children, let us not love with words or tongue but with actions and in truth."

The One Anothers give us a practical agenda for how we can love one another.

The opposite of love is not hate. The opposite of love is indifference.

Group Time—Session Nine

Each member of the group should give his or her individual response to the first three questions. Allow about two minutes for each person's response. Allow all group members to share their answer to question #1 before proceeding to question #2.

1. What was the most interesting concept in this chapter?

2. Referring back to last week's lesson, share about a time this week when you were able to forgive someone else and a time when you should have forgiven someone else but did not.

3. Share your responses to the first three Personal Journal entries in this chapter (page 123).

As a group, process these discussion questions: [These discussion questions have been prioritized. Depending on the time allotted for your group discussion, you may not be able to process all the questions.]

a. Proverbs 28:23 says, "He who rebukes a man will in the end gain more favor than he who has a flattering tongue." How can admonishing someone actually be an act of love?

b. It's been said that learning is primarily a function of timing; we learn more quickly when we need to know something and sense that the knowledge is applicable to our lives. How does this relate to our need to be sensitive to the *timing* of when we admonish others, particularly when we want to instruct someone (as opposed to needing to warn or correct)?

c. Read 1 Samuel 2:12–17, 22–25 and 3:13. What was lacking in Eli's rebuke of his two sons?

d. What can we do if the person we're admonishing doesn't receive us?

e. How does the issue of being approachable relate to the ministry of admonishing one another?

f. If we're not willing to engage in the ministry of admonishing others, what might we be tempted to do (e.g., complain about them, gossip, become bitter, write them off)? What are the advantages of being forthright and honest with someone who needs to be admonished as opposed to ignoring an issue and letting it build up?

g. How does Ephesians 4:15 speak to this issue of admonishing others?

h. In 1 Timothy 1:3 Paul tells Timothy to admonish certain teachers in Ephesus because they were teaching false doctrine. In 2 Timothy 1:7 Paul encourages Timothy not to be timid about his calling and gifts. We're not sure what he was being timid about but perhaps it was related to having to admonish men who were older than him. Why is it often hard to admonish others, particularly those who are older?

i. Hebrews 12:6 says that the Lord disciplines those he loves. Proverbs 27:6 says that, "The kisses of an enemy may be profuse, but faithful are the wounds of a friend." What is the connection between loving someone and being willing to admonish them?

j. How will admonishing others be a testimony to "all men" (John 13:34) that we belong to the Lord and that we are his disciples?

k. On a scale from 1 to 10 (1 being, "We're not too good at this" and 10 being, "We're really good at this"), how good is your church/organization at admonishing people?

Homework:

Read and process chapter 10.

EIGHT MORE ONE ANOTHERS

In this chapter, we're going to briefly discuss eight more One Anothers. They are covered in detail in the sequel to this workbook (the second workbook of the 11th Commandment series). The following discussion should at least introduce the concepts and challenge you to begin sharing eight more expressions of God's love.

Wait for One Another

"Wait for each other" (1 Corinthians 11:33).

While I was writing this workbook, I continually ask the Lord to help me experience what I was writing. I wanted to understand each of the One Anothers in a deeper way than I ever had before. I vividly remember the day he taught me about Wait for One Another.

I had taken a small group of friends to New York City for four days, just to see the sights and sounds of the big city. There's a lot to see in the Big Apple, so each day's itinerary was well orchestrated and full.

In New York City if you're traveling less than twenty blocks, the preferred mode of transportation is walking. And the pace is quick. So on the first day we were shuffling from one place to the next, maintaining a quick pace as we went. One member of our group was an older lady who had trouble walking fast. Her daughter was in the group, so the two of them would walk together. The rest of our group would inevitably get several blocks ahead of them and then have to stop and wait. I felt myself getting irritated at the constant delays, thinking to myself, *This isn't fair. We have a lot to see and do, and the pace of the entire group should not be set by one slow person.*

The lady's daughter became exasperated at the pressure to keep the pace. She finally said, "Don, we just can't keep up. You're going too fast. Just go on without us." At that moment, the Lord said to me, as clearly as if it were displayed on a billboard in Times Square—*Wait for One Another.*

I accepted the Lord's rebuke, slowed down, and for the rest of the trip we adopted her pace. I actually enjoyed the trip more, not only because you can absorb more at a slower pace, but because there is joy in ministering the One Anothers, even waiting!

When we Wait for One Another, we decide to abandon our own pace, agenda, abilities, strengths, and desires and yield to others. It is a practical and challenging derivative of Prefer One Another.

Sometimes we are called on to wait for the fears and weaknesses of others. My wife is afraid of storms and bad weather. At times we have cancelled plans because she was reluctant to leave the house and get out in bad weather. I am tempted to say, "I'm not going to let someone else's fear control my life," but then a gentle nudging from the Spirit says—*Wait for One Another.*

In our struggle to Wait for One Another, we will encounter an ugly vice called impatience.

Do you remember the Bible story about the time when God told the Israelites to enter the Promised Land? Prior to leading the whole nation in, Moses sent twelve men to explore the land. When they returned, ten of the men gave a pessimistic report; the bottom line was, "We can't do it." Two of the men, Joshua and Caleb, said just the opposite: "God has given us the land, we can do it!" The people chose to listen to the ten so they wandered in the desert for forty years. Why did the ten spies have to wander for forty years? Because of unbelief. Why did the entire nation wander for forty years? Because they believed a bad report. Why did Joshua and Caleb wander for forty years? Because they wanted to be with the people they loved—they were willing to wait.

In our struggle to Wait for One Another, we will encounter an ugly vice called impatience. Impatience is a close relative of selfishness. We often become impatient when faced with irritations or opposition but we are sorely tempted with impatience when faced with delay. We just don't want to slow down.

The antiquated train on a branch line was creeping slowly through the countryside when suddenly it came to a dead stop. The only passenger in the car, a salesman riding the line for the first time, asked the conductor why they had stopped. The conductor said, "Nothing to worry about, sir. There's a cow on the tracks." In about ten minutes, the train got under way again, but after chugging along for a mile or two, it again ground to a halt. "Just a temporary delay," the conductor said. "We'll be on our way shortly." The exasperated salesman asked, "What is it now? Did we catch up to the cow again?"

In life, there will be many cows on the tracks. They can be seen as irritating hindrances to our well-planned itineraries, in which case we will justify ignoring them and continuing on at our own pace, or, they can be seen as divine opportunities to share a little grace by Waiting for One Another.

Write about a time when someone waited for you.

_____

Write about a time when you recently waited for someone else.

_____

Write about a time when you should have waited for someone but didn't.

_____

Offer Hospitality to One Another

"Offer hospitality to one another" (1 Peter 4:9).

Alice James, wife of William James, says that often during evenings her husband would exclaim, "Are we never to have an evening alone? Must we always talk to people every night?" And she would answer, "I will see that whoever calls tonight is told that you are strictly engaged." So they would settle down to their quiet evening. Presently the doorbell would ring and Alice would go to the entry, making sure that her instructions were carried out; but close behind her would be William, exclaiming, "Come in! Come right in!"

God's people should be hospitable. We should be gracious hosts. We should be given to generous and cordial reception of guests. We should continually offer a pleasant environment.

There's nothing mysterious about this One Another; it is entirely practical. It simply means: Have people over to your house for fellowship and a meal. Always be gracious and kind when meeting new people. Fellowship often around drink and a meal.

At a church I once served, we developed a simple but effective strategy for the members of a large Bible study class to get to know one another on a deeper level. There were about one hundred members in the class, so we solicited eleven couples to host a covered-dish dinner in their homes. We then randomly assigned everyone in the class to a host home. The agenda for the evening was simple: Share a meal together, get to know one another better, and pray for each other. This simple exercise yielded tremendous results: oneness and care for one another increased. We made it a bi-annual event.

Planned events are profitable, but our *spirit* of hospitality should be spontaneous and eager. Initially we may need some prodding, but eventually our desire to be hospitable should be natural and unstructured. Our homes should be frequented by friends and strangers (Hebrews 13:2).

> God's people should be hospitable. We should be gracious hosts. We should be given to generous and cordial reception of guests. We should continually offer a pleasant environment.

Throughout this workbook I have used my mother as an example of how I saw the One Anothers lived out. Indeed, Mom was given to hospitality. Her desire to be hospitable was continually stymied by my father, who was an emotionally reclusive person and preferred that our house not be open to others. This saddens me. But I do remember the times when Dad gave his approval and Mom was able to entertain guests. She loved cooking a big meal, watching people talk and laugh together, and then engage in after-dinner games. I want to be like Mom.

In your family of origin, did your parents entertain frequently? _____

If so, describe those times.

_____

Do you frequently show hospitality to others? If not, why not?

_____

In recent years, who has shown hospitality to you? _____

Schedule a time in the near future when you can entertain some people.

Date _____

Place _____

Invitation list _____

Pray for One Another
"Pray for each another" (James 5:16).

One Sunday night in April 1912, an American woman was very weary, yet she could not sleep because her spirit was troubled. She felt a burden to pray, so with tremendous earnestness she began to pray for her husband, then in the mid-Atlantic, homeward bound on the *Titanic*. As the hours went by she could get no assurance, so she kept on praying until about five o'clock in the morning when a great peace possessed her and she slept.

Meanwhile her husband, Colonel Gracie, was among the doomed hundreds who were trying frantically to launch the lifeboats from the great ship whose vitals had been torn out by an iceberg. He had given up all hope of being saved himself and was doing his best to help the women and children. He wished that he could get a last message through to his wife, and cried from his heart, "Good-bye, my darling." Then as the ship plunged to her watery grave, he was sucked down in the giant whirlpool. Instinctively he began to swim under water, ice cold as it was, crying in his heart.

Suddenly he came to the surface and found himself near an overturned lifeboat. Along with several others he climbed aboard and was picked up by another lifeboat about five o'clock in the morning, the very time that peace came to his praying wife.

This is a rather dramatic example of the value of praying for others. Personally, I've never had such a spectacular, timely answer to prayer. (Although I suspect that I have indeed; I'm just not aware of it.) But I can recall hundreds of times when Pray for One Another was just the right expression of grace.

- I prayed for many years for the woman who would become my wife, and God gave me Mary.
- I prayed that my daughter would get accepted into just the right college, and she did.
- I prayed that my friend would survive surgery, and he's alive and well.
- I prayed that my co-worker would be delivered from depression, and she was.
- I prayed that my friend's daughter would live, and she didn't. But I'm still glad I prayed.

In this short chapter, I do not feel compelled, nor do I have the space, to comment on the virtues of prayer. Quite frankly, I'm not sure that we need to be convinced of the efficacy of prayer. Nor do we need instruction on how to pray. We just need to do it.

As with all the other One Anothers, Christ is not asking us to do something that he has not and is not doing for us. The apostle Paul assured us that Christ is "at the right hand of God and is also interceding for us" (Romans 8:34). This blessed thought caused Robert McCheyne to say, "If I could hear Christ praying for me in the next room, I would not fear a million enemies. Yet distance makes no difference. He is praying for me."

Make a list of people for whom you would like to pray. Pray for them right now.

Names: _____

_____

_____

Rejoice with One Another

"Rejoice with those who rejoice" (Romans 12:15).

Romans 12:15 states two simple but profound truths: When someone is sad, we should be sad with her (Comfort One Another), and when someone is happy, we should be happy with her (Rejoice with One Another). This one verse covers both sides of the emotional gamut. At any given moment, we are sad, happy, or somewhere in-between.

When people express a strong emotion, we must respond with an emotion. To respond with logic and reasoning leaves them feeling empty and dissatisfied. And not only should we respond with an emotion, we should respond with the *same* emotion. The apostle Paul reiterated this truth in 1 Corinthians 12:26: "If one part suffers, every part suffers with it; if one part is honored, every part rejoices with it." So when someone is on the suffering side of the scale, we respond with like emotion as we do when someone is on the happy side. A poet said it this way, "A sorrow shared is half the sorrow, while a joy shared is twice the joy."

As with all of the One Anothers, rejoicing with people requires that we prefer others. It means that we voluntarily leave our emotional world, enter into their emotional world, and embrace how they're feeling.

It's quite frustrating to be happy on the inside but not have anyone to share it with. Several years ago, my youngest daughter applied to the Julliard School in New York City. It is, arguably, the finest arts school in the world, so it's very difficult to get in. Twelve hundred students auditioned for the theatre department that year, and they only accept twenty. After the initial audition, they immediately call back around 150 students for a second round of interviews. Then you have to wait several months for the final decision. Sarah was elated when she was called back, but then we entered the dreaded waiting period before the final decision was made.

Finally, the call came, and she heard those magical words, "Sarah, we would like for you to be a student at Julliard." Pure bliss. Unadulterated joy. The only downside was—she was home alone. She didn't have anyone to dance with. She tried to call me at the office but I was out, and so were Mary and Lauren. She was ecstatically happy but had no one to rejoice with her. I think we made up for it later, but I do regret that, initially, she had to celebrate alone.

What was the best thing that happened to you last week?

_____

Did you share it with anyone? How did they react?

_____

Think back over the past week. Did you miss the opportunity to rejoice with someone who was rejoicing?

_____

Be Kind to One Another   *(1/18*

"Be kind ... to one another" (Ephesians 4:32).

As Gandhi stepped aboard a train one day, one of his shoes slipped off and landed on the track. He was unable to retrieve it as the train had already begun to move. To the amazement of his companions, Gandhi calmly took off his other shoe and threw it back along the track to land close to the first. Asked by a fellow passenger why he did so, Gandhi smiled. "The poor man who finds the shoe lying on the track," he replied, "will now have a pair he can use."[1]

One of the highest compliments we can receive is for someone to say about us, "He is a kind person." It's possible to be correct but not kind, to be orthodox but lack grace, and even to be truthful but hurtful at the same time. Kindness is the attitude of grace.

Many years ago Dwight W. Morrow, the father of Anne Lindburgh, told a group of friends that Calvin Coolidge had real presidential possibilities. They disagreed, saying that Coolidge was too quiet and lacked color and political personality. "No one would like him," objected one of the group.

But up piped little Anne, then age six: "I like Mr. Coolidge." Then she displayed a finger with a bit of adhesive tape on it. "He was the only one who asked me about my sore finger."

Mr. Morrow nodded. "There's your answer," he said.[2]

The Greek word for "be kind" is *chrestos*, which means "to furnish what is needed and useful, to be profitable."

God's kindness led us to repentance (Romans 2:4), and we are encouraged to "grow up in our salvation" as we taste of the Lord's goodness (1 Peter 2:2–3).

Kindness is a fruit of being filled with the Holy Spirit (Galatians 5:22), and it should be a constant factor in our lives, "Always try to be kind to each other and to everyone else" (1 Thessalonians 5:15).

It's possible to be correct but not kind,

to be orthodox but lack grace,
and even to be truthful but hurtful at the same time.
Kindness is the attitude of grace.

Honor One Another   *11/18*

"Honor one another" (Romans 12:10).

We can Honor One Another in various ways.

I respect you. We should be quick to solicit people's ideas and opinions and, when appropriate, acquiesce to their thoughts. The general rule of thumb is: When we are about to make a decision that will affect other people's lives, we need to ask their opinion.

I recognize who you are—your gifts and talents. We should strive to understand the unique contribution that each person can make to the community and then acknowledge that potential and provide the opportunity for each person to function in his or her strength.

Jesus was not able to do many miracles in his hometown because "Only in his home town and in his own house is a prophet *without honor*" (Matthew 13:57; emphasis added). The people of Nazareth did not recognize Jesus (honor him) as who he was—the Son of God. Therefore he was not able to be who he was and do what he did best among them.

I submit to your authority. We honor those who are in authority over us by submitting to them.

Ephesians 6:2 instructs us, "Honor your father and mother." Likewise, 1 Peter 2:17 commands us to "honor the king."

I value and esteem you. We honor people by recognizing their great value and treating them accordingly.

Do you properly respect other people? Are you quick to solicit other people's opinions and input?

_____

How do you honor those who are in authority over you?

_____

How do you recognize the gifts and talents of those closest to you?

_____

Confess Your Sins to One Another

"Confess your sins to each another" (James 5:16).

One day while passing a house of ill fame, Socrates, the famous Greek thinker, noticed one of his students inside. Stepping to the doorway, Socrates called out to his disciple. The latter hid himself, as Adam did when he committed the first sin. However, the youth eventually had to come before his mentor, his face was crimson with shame. He hung his head, expecting a stern rebuke from his teacher. But Socrates spoke in the tones of a true father: "Come forth, my son, I pray you, come forth! To leave this house is not disgraceful; the only disgraceful thing was to have entered it."[3]

When we have sinned, the best thing to do is to "come forth." We need to confess. But instead of confessing our sins, we are usually tempted to justify ourselves, rationalize our actions, or blame others. But the only way to remove our guilt and bring healing to relationships is to confess.

No doubt, it is hard to do. The words, "I was wrong. Would you forgive me?" don't naturally spill from our lips. But we must learn to say them.

When was the last time you confessed to someone? Write about it here.

_____

_____

When was the last time someone confessed to you? Write about it here.

_____

_____

Be Devoted to One Another   (1/25

"Be devoted to one another" (Romans 12:10).

Soon after Jack Benny died, George Burns was interviewed on TV. "Jack and I had a wonderful friendship for nearly fifty-five years," Burns said. "Jack never walked out on me when I sang a song, and I never walked out on him when he played the violin. We laughed together, we played together, we worked together, and we ate together. I suppose that for many of those years we talked every single day."[4]

The Greek word for "devotion" is *philostorgos*, which means "to cherish one's kindred, to be fond of, to be fraternal toward fellow Christians, tenderly loving, and tenderly affectionate."

Devotion implies a deep level of commitment. It is perhaps, the only One Another which we can, in some measure, ration out.

Through the years, I have sensed that I have developed a deep sense of devotion to certain individuals, but not to everyone. For instance, my highest devotion is to my wife and children. I think that is expected. Even among my friends, I am more devoted to some than others. This may smack of favoritism, but my conscience doesn't bother me in the least.

> Devotion implies a deep level of commitment. It is perhaps, the only One Another which we can, in some measure, ration out.

It seems as if the Lord also had those to whom he was deeply devoted, the twelve disciples. Even among the twelve he had three whom he seemed to confide in (Peter, James, and John), and some would even suggest that he had a favorite among the three (John). He didn't love them any more than the others, but he did feel called to spend more time with them, and he allowed them to know him in ways the others didn't. The three were invited to be with him on the Mount of Transfiguration, which was perhaps the highlight of his earthly ministry, and in the Garden of Gethsemane, which was arguably the lowest point in his earthly ministry.

So in the course of life, we'll sense a natural yearning to be devoted to certain people. In my thirty years of ministry I have served on the staff of many large churches. If I counted up their combined membership it would be in the tens of thousands. I don't feel strongly obliged to maintain a close relationship with all of them, but there are a handful for which I would drop what I'm doing and respond to their needs in a moment's notice.

To be devoted to someone implies:

1. Value—"I highly value you, both as a person, my _____ [wife, son, daughter, etc.], and as a friend. You are important to me."
2. Commitment—"I am committed to you. I pledge to be involved in your life."
3. Long-term commitment—"I'm in this relationship for the long haul. I'll walk with you through the good times and the bad. We are friends for life."
4. Focus—"While there are many things that compete for my attention, you are always in my line of sight. When your life situation demands it, you will be the sole focus of my attention."
5. Priority—"My life, like yours, is multifaceted. But I want you to know that you are a priority to me. I always prioritize relationships over things and events, and I'll always prioritize you."
6. Meeting needs—"I am aware of your physical and emotional needs and want to be a part of meeting those needs."
7. Faithfulness—"Mentally and emotionally, I'm going to 'handcuff' myself to you. I hope my relational tenacity will make you feel loved and secure."
8. A deep, thorough knowing—"I want to get to know you on a deep, intimate level. I also want to know your immediate family."
9. Vulnerable disclosure—"I am willing to share with you the deep issues of my life."
10. Tenderness—"You are very dear to me. I want to care for you like a mother hen cares for her chicks."
11. Consistency—"You can count on me to be a consistent source of love and care."

Out of the furnaces of war come many true stories of sacrificial friendship. One such story tells of two friends in World War I, who were inseparable. They enlisted together, trained together, were shipped overseas together, and fought side by side in the trenches. During an attack, one of the men was critically wounded in a field filled with barbed wire obstacles, and he was unable to crawl back to his foxhole. The entire area was under a withering enemy crossfire, and it was suicidal to try to reach him. Yet his friend decided to try. Before he could get out of his own trench, his sergeant yanked him back and ordered him not to go. "It's too late. You can't do him any good, and you'll only get yourself killed."

A few minutes later, the officer turned his back, and instantly the man was gone after his friend. A few minutes later, he staggered back, mortally wounded, with his friend, now dead, in his arms. The sergeant was both angry and deeply moved. "What a waste," he blurted out. "He's dead, and you're dying. It just wasn't worth it."

With almost his last breath, the dying man replied, "Oh, yes, it was, Sarge. When I got to him, the only thing he said was, 'I knew you'd come, Jim!'"[5]

1. Name some of your long-term friends. Do they sense that you are devoted to them?

_____

2. In your life, who has demonstrated that they are devoted to you?

_____

3. Name some of the people you would like to be devoted to.

_____

ENDWORD

The Tomb of the Unknown soldier in Arlington National Cemetery in Washington, DC, has a guard 24 hours a day. Every hour on the hour, 365 days a year, a new solder reports for duty. When the new guard arrives, he receives his orders from the one who is leaving. The words are always the same: "Orders Remain Unchanged." [6]

Two-thousand years ago Jesus issued a clear, certain command—Love One Another. While much has changed during the two millennia, his directive has not. His "Orders Remain Unchanged."

And the command is refreshingly simple. In the midst of a complex often confusing world, Jesus calls us to simply focus on one thing—sharing his love with others. It is a command which, when obeyed, brings joy to all.

THE 11TH COMMANDMENT PROJECT

The 11th Commandment Project is a work in progress!

- It is a continuously expanding group of individuals who are committed to loving others.
- It is a growing network of churches who offer an ongoing 11th Commandment ministry.
- It is an expanding set of resources that help communicate the 11th Commandment message.

You can be involved in this strategic movement!

- Share the 11th Commandment message with others.

- Lead a small group of friends through a nine-week course.

- Share a copy of the workbook with friends in other churches.

- Help start an ongoing 11th Commandment ministry in your church.

- Share the project with your church staff.

- Volunteer to serve in your local church ministry.

- Contribute to one of the 11th Commandment resources.

We're currently developing a new resource that will be a collection of real-life stories that illustrate how the One Anothers touched someone's life. We welcome your submission of a personal story. Your story could tell how you were blessed by ministering a One Another to someone else, or how you were the recipient of someone else's ministry. For instance, we recently received this story, which speaks poignantly about Preferring One Another.

"Twice a year our church has a special youth worship service which the students lead. A young person leads congregational singing, another shares a devotional, another prays, and many present special music.

"For one of the services, a young girl was scheduled to play a flute solo, but the day before, she dropped her flute and bent it. Because it was the weekend, she couldn't get the flute fixed, so her father had to rent one. The rental instrument was a cheap student model that sounded pretty bad.

"On Sunday afternoon during rehearsal, another young lady who played flute in the youth orchestra heard about what had happened. She had a brand-new Selmer flute (which is a fine instrument). She offered her new flute to her friend who was going to play a solo, not just for that one piece, but for the entire evening.

The young girl's thoughtfulness was a wonderful expression of Prefer One Another."

Send your One Another illustrations to:
2322 Creekside Circle South, Irving, Texas, 75063 or e-mail to 6Acts@6Acts.org

If you want more information about the 11th Commandment Project,
contact us at the above address, visit us at www.6Acts.org or call 972.432.8690.

NOTES

Chapter 1: The 11th Commandment
1. From Charles Allen, *What I Have Lived By*, quoted in James Hewitt, *Illustrations Unlimited* (Wheaton, Ill.: Tyndale, 1988), 118.
2. *The Wittenburg Door*, quoted in Charles Swindoll, *The Tale of the Tardy Oxcart* (Nashville: Word, 1998), 567.
3. Tony Campolo, *Who Switched the Price Tags?*, quoted in Swindoll, *The Tale of the Tardy Oxcart*, 6–7.

Chapter 2: Prefer One Another
1. Paul Lee Tan, *Encyclopedia of 7700 Illustrations*, quoted in Swindoll, *The Tale of the Tardy Oxcart*, 221.
2. Hewitt, *Illustrations Unlimited*, 450.

Chapter 3: Accept One Another
3. Ray Stedman, *The Birth of the Body*, quoted in Swindoll, *The Tale of the Tardy Oxcart*, 8.
4. Gladys Hunt, quoted in Eternity magazine, October 1999.

Chapter 4: Greet One Another
1. Peggy Noonan, *Character Above All*, quoted in Swindoll, *The Tale of the Tardy Oxcart*, 113.
2. Dale Carnegie, *How to Win Friends and Influence People* (New York: Pocket Books, 1936), 73.
3. Ibid., 82–83.

Chapter 5: Encourage One Another
1. Hewitt, *Illustrations Unlimited*, 227.
2. Paul Lee Tan, *Encyclopedia of 7700 Illustrations* (Rockville, Md.: Assurance Publishers, 1979), 1976.
3. Dennis Waitley, Seeds of Greatness, quoted in *The Tale of the Tardy Oxcart*, 112.

Chapter 6: Comfort One Another
1. Quoted in Hewitt, *Illustrations Unlimited*, 113.
2. J. H. Jowett, quoted in George Sweeting, *Great Quotes and Illustrations* (Waco, TX.: Word Books, 1985), 64.
3. *Preaching* (March–April 1991), quoted in Swindoll, *The Tale of the Tardy Oxcart*.

Chapter 7: Carry One Another's Burdens
1. From a letter by Andrew C. Davison, quoted in Hewitt, *Illustrations Unlimited*.
2. Source unknown.
3. Olga Wetzel, "Bus Ride," *Eternity* (February 1977).
4. Gordon MacDonald, from sermon "Pointing to Jesus: Generosity," preached at Grace Chapel, Lexington, Massachusetts (February 22, 1998).

Chapter 8: Forgive One Another
1. Quoted in Hewitt, *Illustrations Unlimited*, 218.
2. Ibid., 222.
3. Ibid., 218.

Chapter 10: Eight More One Anothers
1. Author unknown, quoted in *The Little Brown Book of Anecdotes*, quoted in Swindoll, *The Tale of the Tardy Oxcart*, 330.
2. Paul Lee Tan, *Encyclopedia of 7700 Illustrations*, 705.
3. Ibid., 1134.
4. Alan Loy McGinnis, *The Friendship Factor*, quoted in Swindoll, *The Tale of the Tardy Oxcart*, 220.
5. Gary Irving, *Quality Friendships*, quoted in Swindoll, *The Tale of the Tardy Oxcart*, 222.
6. *Our Daily Bread*, August 24, 2000.